# Southword *41*

Southword is published
by Southword Editions
an imprint of the
Munster Literature Centre
Frank O'Connor House
84 Douglas Street
Cork City T12 X802
Ireland

www.munsterlit.ie

 @MunLitCentre

 /southwordjournal

 /munsterliteraturecentre

#Southword

Issue 41
ISBN 978-1-905002-87-0

**Editor**
Patrick Cotter

**Fiction Editor**
Billy O'Callaghan

**Production**
James O'Leary

Thank you to Anne Kennedy for her technical assistance

Cover image: *'Tobar' ('Well')* by Peadar Lamb

*The Munster Literature Centre is a grateful recipient of funding from*

Comhairle Cathrach Chorcaí
Cork City Council

# CONTENTS

# PLEASE SUBSCRIBE

By subscribing, you will receive new issues of *Southword* straight from the printers, as quickly as we will ourselves. Your subscription will also help to provide us with the resources to make *Southword* even better.

*Rates for two issues per year:*

| | |
|---|---|
| Ireland, UK, USA | €20 *postage free* |
| Germany, France, Italy, Spain | €24 *postage free, tax-inclusive* |
| Rest of the world | €30 *postage included* |

For subscriptions and renewals visit www.munsterlit.ie — payment accepted by PayPal.

*Southword* may also be purchased issue-by-issue through Amazon outlets worldwide and select book shops in Ireland, the UK, Europe and the USA. We keep an up-to-date list of supporting book shops on the www.munsterlit.ie subscriptions page.

# THREE POEMS
# Bernadette McCarthy

---

'INSIDE AFRICA' STORE, SHANDON STREET

Sweetened cabin biscuits, frozen ugwu and fresh bitterleaf—
I long to remember ~~my~~ your life, that flickers like a light
on the dial of the four-faced liar. ~~Google~~ I led you to this shop,

your first time in what an old fella called 'the real capital'.
I scan the tins of pears that line the plyboard shelves
like bloated bigots. 'This weather's ~~bipolar~~ mixed up,' you say,

'it doesn't know whether to rain or shine'. You tell me
about the long, dry winter before, how you tried to kill
yourself twice, I tell you ~~about the pills I'm taking~~ to keep dreaming

and we talk of prophetic dreams, the proximity of St Colman's cemetery
to your ~~prison's~~ centre's sliding door. We long to take chalk and sketch
each other's childhoods—porridge, piseógs, the ~~killers~~ friends that called,

your Nigeria, ~~your~~ my Cork, where our children will not walk as we walked,
or speak as we spoke—and we rush, before the parking disc expires,
to bring our bulging, motherly bags back ~~home.~~

## GEARAGH

Catkins are only a dream now. I tease the bearded
trunk. It takes centuries for lichen to grow this thick
and just a moment to rip it off. The twigs criss-cross
like country cousins, brackets fumble at each other along
the maimed bark. Whoopers honk from the reservoir and a blackbird
retorts: he knows through his mother's blood that thousands of broods ago
the trees stretched from here to Gougane Barra. *Gaorthadh*, the wooded
(wounded) river valley. Ballingeary, Garrynapeaka. Island after drowned
island catching on the lip-weirs, scrambling for the source: *Lee, Laoi, Lua.*

Note: The Gearagh is a post-glacial alluvial forest in Co. Cork,
much of which was submerged by the flooding of the Lee Valley.

THE QUARRY LAKE

The dull depths smack off the smooth, shaved rock,
lulling me into forgetting all but the trampled water-mint
until you plunge naked towards the quarry bottom,
skinning the quivering sky into lake.

Thrashing the gunmetal water with tanned arms,
you swim out beyond the midges, diving, but never deep enough
to see the winding-engine left behind,
too heavy to haul up before the Lee was dammed.

*'Twas a shame too.* The stories bloom like algae after slurry.
How the furnace burning limestone and bog-deal
could be seen nearly all the way to Cork;
how kids crossed to school on stilts, and when the river burst

they'd gather salmon stranded in the meadows.
How the ESB used row-boats to navigate the wetland,
cut the great oaks where woodkerne took cover,
broke houses down, salvaged metal and glass.

Crowds gathered on Sleaveen to watch the waters rise,
isle after clearfelled isle submitting to progress.
*I walked where fish swim.* It was a thorough job
but for one fella who wouldn't leave

though the waters lapped at the sashes,
took a coracle to town each Sunday till the night of the big storm.
A rose clambers up a yew by a hollow where a cottage stood;
a cadet was kept in a cowhouse for a week,

telling tales of Flanders and his woman in Macroom
so that his minders grew fond of him, would have let him live
(or so I heard in the pub), till the command from the boys above.
They say the man in the squad with the only loaded gun

didn't pull the trigger. The commander whipped a pistol out instead —
a quick clean shot to the side of the auxie's head.
Someone took his boots and belt before they put him in the bog.
*'Twould have been a shame to just let them rot.*

A heron takes off from a sally clump, once a tower in the limeworks,
now crannog for a petty king. I'd join you, but there is no trusted edge
to lure this weaker swimmer in. Swans whoop like men lost
within the army of drowned stumps. *Don't dive too deep.*

# WAVES
## Fenella O'Regan

---

My hair drowned me. Or so my mum used to say. It weighed me down – a millstone around my neck, and face, dragging me down in a sea of other long-haired girls. Long and thick, coppery brown – it shone gold when the light hit it in a certain way, at a certain point in the day. I wore it down to my waist for years, longer when it was straightened. Or when I straightened my back, and stood up correctly with shoulders over hips and hips over knees. My hair was wiry and coarse like the fibres of a rope and looked precisely so when I wore it hanging down in a heavy plait, between my shoulder blades. Shampoo ads would describe my hair texture as unruly, though I would argue that it was anything but – what with enough conditioner to smooth down the halo of frizz that erupted around my temples. It was wavy – at least I had trained it to become so. It was easy to manipulate and held form well. I could gather it up into a bun without the need for an elastic. And, when I sat watching television or in assembly, distractedly winding locks around my fingers, I would stand up with perfectly fashioned barrel ringlets. Absent minded fiddling gave me the effortless waves that women spend copious amounts of time and money crafting from heat and a concoction called "salt spray." Soft, springy curls that did not grow limp and perspire or stiffen under hairspray, my hair was the object of much unspoken envy; the image of an Austen protagonist in a school uniform. Rather than overwhelming me, I believed that my hair kept me afloat in the tumult that was an all-girls secondary school. Good hair was the only parallel that could be drawn between the popular girls and I. My one redeeming feature. To cut it all off would be sacrilegious, a betrayal to the sisterhood, a rejection of the beauty standards we were all expected to abide by – regardless of the cost and effort. And the time spent painstakingly combing it. The pain of combing it, in general. My ringlets were a life ring, their bounce a buoy to clamber onto.

My older cousin Rosie was once, quite literally, almost drowned by her hair. Hers was wild and beachy, like my own, by virtue of the fact she grew up on the beaches of west Kerry; where the wind whipped the wisps of hair that escaped from her ponytail and the dried salt bound each knotted strand to the next. We cousins would go out surfing and sailing, body boarding on the grey green sea. Our pale faces bopping, barely visible amongst the white horses cantering across the water's surface. Out into the sea we barrelled, fearlessly, as weightless on land as we were on water – scarcely breaking the hardened crust of sand that had formed overnight. Our footprints indiscernible. Water babies, we waded out in all weathers. We swam when the sea was as flat and still as a ream of satin, our strokes slicing through it as clean as a seamstress's scissors. Or when the rain fell hard, like rubber bullets. We dove into waves, into their hungry mouths that snapped shut behind us. We were pummelled and flipped, pulled down into the belly of the beast – only to emerge as sea foam frothed around us, snorting and spluttering. Deaf to the chortles of the others, ears and noses blocked with seawater. Laughter, and cries, often get lost at sea; carried by the wind or drowned out by its howl. We relied on our other senses out there, on the water. Something primeval descended upon me with each step, as I lowered myself into its crystalline depths. To be in water – and at one with water – was the most elemental thing of all; its ebb and flow resonating with me. We were on the same wavelength. I could feel the sea swell as it carried me in on the crest of a wave and a flimsy bit of carbon fibre. I could feel the pull of the tide as the wave that delivered me to the shoreline, dragged me back out again. I could see the cords of water tighten at around my ankles when, plunging them into the wet sand, I stood stock still – trying to stop the tide and time. I could see my orange towel on the beach, there, where I had entered the sea, how far I was from that and how close I had drifted to the rocks. But I could not see Rosie. I could not hear her, none of us could.

The sea was choppy. It had begun to rain, falling in great, glutinous drops, collecting on my eyelashes and blurring my vision. The already grey expanse of sky and sea was greyer still. Running down the bridge of my nose and incessantly drip-drip-dripping from tip to lip, I remember trying to wipe the rain away, trying to stem the flow. Often, I would catch the rain on my tongue. I loved the smell of it, the sweet fragrant taste of it. But this time, my mouth only opened wide enough to release a thin, reedy yell. My lips were dry and cracked, gritted with sand that collected in the corners, nicking the now blue tinged flesh. Licked raw by the wind and sea and my own tongue – leaving only a residual layer of salt – my lips stung like a thousand knives. Yet, all I could feel was the one great knife wedged in my chest, wriggling from side to side between my ribs, plunging ever deeper. Fear was beginning to sink in. It was then I realised how deep the water had got. We were well out of our depth – Rosie, too, despite being the strongest swimmer between us. We had been pushed far out, I thought as I pushed furiously back to the shore, not stopping until I could feel the smoothness of the pebbles beneath my feet. They shifted under my weight as I scanned the surf for Rosie's seal-slick head. Waist-deep now, I waved my arms frantically to alert those on the shore that we needed assistance. Could they see us when I couldn't see them? Horizontal rain beat against my chest as my heart pounded straight back at it. Blood drummed in my ears, silencing the crash of waves into the water as they surged together towards the shore. Blindly, thrashing in the shallows I caught sight of a red foamboard, lapping in the tide. Tossed high, it met breaking waves head-on, never drifting from the spot or washing up on the sand. Like a kite flown directly into headwinds, it struggled, trying desperately to tear itself away from that which was anchoring it below. The plastic cord strained as the insubstantial raft flipped over and back, drumming a low rhythmic beat against the taut skin of the sea - almost like Morse Code. It called out to me to be freed.

I like to pathologise my finding Rosie that day, her body pinned beneath board, as a symbol of our uncommonly close bond. Less than a year separated us but were united by far more; the smattering of indiscriminate freckles across our faces, the piercing cool blue of our eyes that flashed white hot when enraged, the aforementioned russet-coloured curls and our unquenchable thirst for the sea. But, it was merely happenchance that I found her that day. I was in the right place at the right time inasmuch as she was in the wrong one. Like us, one wave was followed in quick succession by another that matched it in power and intensity. She was caught between the two which coalesced into one. The tail of the lightweight board was lifted by the combined force of the waves causing the head, to which Rosie clung, to be driven down under the water. From below, she was trapped in a tailspin as one wave rolled into the next. Disorientated, the only way to distinguish up from down was by the light that penetrated through the clouds of white foam above her. But the sea yearned for Rosie as much as she did for it. The magnetic pull between the two was undeniable. An inseverable tie drew her into its shadowy depths as its tentacles strained to catch her and cradle her to sleep in their clammy embrace. Long lengths of gelatinous green seaweed weaved themselves around her hair, wrenching her downwards. The more she struggled, the harder they yanked. The land and the seabed fought a tireless tug of war for her; the bungee cord fastened around her wrist tried to drag her up to the surface while the seaweed bound her from below. Reeds wrapped around each strand of hair, strangling her like green fingers around a throat. Snakes slowly squeezing the life out of her lungs. She was in their chokehold. Until we cut her free.

Her father – my uncle – wrenched her from the water and along with her limp body, he pulled out the spineless stems that she had struggled against. Root by root. Lying on the cold, wet sand, she reminded me of the formidable Medusa; her beautifully serene face framed by coiling serpents. And like Medusa, as we peered over her motionless body, we were all turned to stone. None of us daring to breathe, to move, until she did. Heavy droplets fell silently to the ground as water ran in rivets down my hair and back, some sliding down my face. Or, perhaps, those were tears. They were salty nonetheless. Rosie did stir again as she did swim again. Although, not that day. Peeling off the neoprene skin, we wrapped her in towels and blankets. She sank shivering into the car, as weak as the tea she sipped on. And as colour returned slowly to her face, the sharpness of the memory dulled, the nearness of the miss forgotten, put down to simply one of those things.

Some of the put downs that she endured during those lazy summer days, when week yawned into week, was due to the vaguely putrid smell that emanated from her upon entering a room. A smell which only grew more fetid the closer she got and the nearer September loomed. The stench was familiar – it was the scent of the sea. But warm. And decaying. She smelt like a particular sea, or beach, rather – Kilshannig Strand in the Maharees. A queasy sea that had coughed up the bilious contents of its stomach and left them strewn, half-buried in the sand, to rot. While some girls returned from their summer holidays with colourful yarns and beads braided into their clean hair, green wisps of seaweed threaded themselves around Rosie's locks. Her hair was matted, tangled with knots and algae and, by the end of summer had felted itself into dreadlocks. She stopped brushing it and allowed strands of seagrass to wrap around her burnished curls, streaks which gleamed viridescent in the sun. As conspicuous as a stray sprig of spinach trapped in one's teeth, yet no one had the good grace to tell her. When freed from their elastic, her tresses stuck together stiffly in one clump – like a tuft of uncut grass burnt by the sun. But no one minded – or even noticed. We were free-range kids, allowed to roam at will from beach to beach on our bikes and by foot. We scrabbled up mountains and over stone walls – scabby kneed and scuffed shoed. I remember tearing fibrous pink rasher meat, pilfered from someone's mother's fridge, into strips and skewering it to fishing hooks, as we cast our makeshift rods over the footbridge. We never caught anything, not even colds – though we would sit there patiently, coatless, as the *bog* rain from the mountains rolled in. Time went as unnoticed as the soft rain that fell as silent as the mist, leaving us sodden and steaming, smelling of damp. We were always slightly grimy – grass stained, sandy toed and fingers jammed with blackberry juice and the occasional thorn, from greedily tearing off the fruit before their time. No parent noticed how unkempt Rosie's hair had got because none noticed her – or any of us – in general. We stayed out from dawn to dusk, coming home caked under a layer of dust. Each one of us indistinguishable from the other. *Strils*, who knew only too well that as soon as September arrived we would have to struggle into straining school uniforms that were never replaced over the summer.

The only reflections we saw for those three months rippled and shimmered under us as we smiled in the sunshine. In the car window, I peered at the face looking back at me, a face I'd largely forgotten. I leaned my cheek against the cool glass. On the uneven road surface, every knock against the window pane was another jolt back to the reality of going home. Gazing moodily out at the rushing landscape, I thought of Rosie. The razed fields of wheat and barley that stretched out either side of the empty road reminded me of her shorn head. As we dragged our suitcases reluctantly out from under the bed, my aunt dragged a brush vainly through her straggly hair. But, although the crown of her head gleamed under the paddle of the brush, from the ears down was a thicket. Bracken-like and untameable. Like a window cast in shadow by overgrown bushes, the only solution was to cut the knotted hair back so not to let Rosie's glowing face be hidden under a bushel. From underneath her jaunty crop, she glowered. With no curtain to hide behind, her resentment for being stripped of her crowning glory, her waterfall of curls, was chiselled into her now stony mien.

Mine cascaded down my back, rippling tawny gold like a waterfall for many summers to come. But, it was very thick, very heavy and even more so after a swim or a shower of rain. It took aeons to dry, and only had it dried than I was back in the ocean, bobbing up and down under the waves, or floating on my back, staring up at the vagrant clouds that drifted in time with me. I envied Rosie's now tousled bob, which she could towel dry in a matter of minutes and how she teased feathered ends to frame her elfin face. I had the same sharp jaw and defiant chin but rather than drawing back the heavy curtain as she had, I chose to shield myself from people's regard behind protective tresses. I was scared of my face. I didn't like it and feared the world wouldn't either. The one thing I was secure in was my own insecurity. Like all teenage girls are. It was easier to keep my head down, let my hair fall into my eyes and mask any feelings of self-doubt behind conformity. I had already stuck my head above the proverbial parapet too much as it was; the safety pin in my ear, the Nirvana tee, the Rastafarian bandana and the various other accoutrements that I got away with sewing ad-hoc onto my uniform. To cut my hair would be seen as too much, too radical. Too butch. In a rural Catholic-ethos school it would be sure to set tongues wagging. My hair — long and wavy — was the one thing that my peers liked about me and thus, the one thing that I liked about myself. To reject their only validation of me would have been social suicide. I saw chopping it all off as the ultimate form of self-harm. It took me years to learn that it is, instead, the greatest emancipation.

At fifteen, I moved to France. I wanted to sever with all that had come before and got the notion, as many women do, that a haircut would allow me to divorce myself from the life I was leaving behind. I wished to be free of that weight which kept me looking down rather than forward and believed that a light head would invite a clear one. What's more, I idolised French women and lusted over that certain *je ne sais quoi* they seemed to exude. To me, a rakish pixie cut was the embodiment of effortless Gallic chic.

Sitting tall and proud in my leatherette throne that day, my unruly curls were brushed a hundred times silky smooth. And, as the hairdresser carefully parted my hair – down the middle with a fine-tooth comb – I parted with my own sense of self that, up to that moment, had been fastened to the surface layer. My external self. The stark white line she had drawn down my scalp symbolised that cleavage as I transitioned from girl to woman. Ironically, to cross across the threshold into womanhood I had to sever all ties with the oldest and greatest vestige of femininity I had ever known. To cut through the thicket, she braided either side into long plaits that only served to remind me of the girlhood I was losing. Staring at myself hard in the mirror, I saw my life in those plaits; a single long length made one by three interwoven strands – past, present, future. But a future that was, nonetheless, inextricably tethered to what was and always had been. I needed a clean cut, a break from the past, to find confidence in myself as a woman, independent from my appearance. I always worried that cutting my hair would leave me with too much face, too much neck. And it's true. Short hair leaves you with nothing to distract people from what you are saying and what you are asking of them. But, by being too much we can show the world we have had enough. The tide has turned, a wave of change upon us.

# FALLING SOFTLY
## Majella Cullinane

---

I first met the sisters outside the Arts building at university in Dublin. They came from the Aran Islands, their first language Irish, and for a city boy like me they seemed as exotic as if they'd been two mermaids washed up on Dún Laoghaire harbour.

The sisters dressed in brightly coloured jumpers and corduroy trousers, or Tie dye pants. They wore brown leather Jesus sandals and thick woollen socks. Both were vegetarian which was rare back then. So much so, I'd to ask them what it meant. I wondered what their fisherman father would have made of his daughters turning their noses up at mackerel and pollack and shark. I imagined their mother sitting by the fire darning socks as she stared out to sea from the kitchen window, listening to her daughters stir in their rooms, thinking about her husband gone well before dawn. I saw her putting turf and wood into the range, and after she had breakfasted heading out on a currach to reunite with her husband at some agreed fishing spot. Their father was an old sea dog of course, weary like Coleridge's ancient mariner, with a long white beard speckled with red, a weathered face, and cool blue eyes that could see beyond the horizon and the ceaseless waves, to an eternity that he could never voice, for there was something secret in the perennial endeavour of fishing, something sacred. I didn't see then how it would have really been. The days in trawlers miles from home, the casting of nets, the repair of nets, the hauling of fish writhing and silver onto the deck, watching them suffocate with air. The sorting and handling, the processing of it. The freezing, cracked hands, the chilblains, the tired, aching muscles, the merged grey of sea and sky.

Deirdre and Grainne were renting a double room out in Cherry Orchard, which was miles from the university, and to get a decent sized place they needed another lodger so an old school friend, Seamus suggested me. It was January, but since the-start-of-term rush was well over, we thought it'd be easier finding a place. As it happened the pickings were slim. We looked at three flats. The first had some kind of strange liquid oozing from the slats of the sitting room floor, most of the door handles were missing, and the landlord looked like he'd just out of prison. The second was D4 luxury and well out of our price range. A renovated Georgian house with sash windows and central heating. The carpet smelled so fresh it was like it'd just come out of the shop that day. The last wasn't far from Ranelagh village, a popular student haunt. The street was nice enough. Red brick terraces mostly, with small gardens and neatly trimmed hedges. The odd spot of squalor along the path with scattered refuge sacks and broken bottles. Number 49 looked reasonably well-presented. A black iron gate and railings around the front. The garden wasn't exactly prize-winning, but tidy at least.

An old man finally answered the door. He wasn't just old. He was ancient. His shoulders were hunched into his chest like a vulture, and he was dressed in a grey blue tweed suit.

'Come in, come in,' he said in a broad accent, and as soon as we stepped inside I wished I'd gasped some air before he closed the door. The smell – a pong really that was part fish, part urine and parts unknown. I thought I'd throw up. Several cats of various colours strode across the hall like a brigade.

'Now,' he said, 'the flat is up those stairs there,' and Deirdre and Grainne followed behind him. 'I'll let you have a look around and I'll be back in a few minutes.'

'It stinks of fish and piss,' I said quietly as soon as he was out of sight.

'Well, if it does Michael I don't get it,' Deirdre said.

'You don't?'

'We're used to the smell of fish,' she said, glaring at me behind her Gandhi glasses.

A scene of familial harmony popped into my mind as I imagined seven girls gutting and filleting fish with the other island women on a wind-swept wharf. Each having held a blade as soon as they could walk.

The old man was back before we knew it, standing on the landing watching us as we roamed around the four large, draughty rooms.

'Where are you from?' he asked Deirdre.

'The Aran Islands.'

'Na hÁrainneacha,' he said, 'Táim ó Chonamara.'

After that I was lost as they started nattering away in Irish. I was useless at Irish.

Even after I left university I used to dream I'd failed Leaving Cert Irish and couldn't go to university. I'd only just passed.

After a few minutes the old man turned to me and glowered. Deirdre smiled, and

I could have sworn I heard her say the word, *dearthair*. She winked at me, and when Grainne caught my eye I could see she was having a hard time not busting herself laughing.

Apart from the pong, the worst thing was the glass cabinet of stuffed pheasants on the landing. I've never been much of a man for birds in a cage, let alone stuffed ones staring out at you with unblinking eyes. If the girls' animal welfare sensibilities were offended they didn't let on as they continued to chat away in Irish.

There was no denying the upstairs, or the flat as it had been designated, would have been something in its day. Traces of its Georgian décor were apparent in the thick, worn carpets, the faded wallpaper and high ceilings, the large mantelpiece, although the fireplace had been closed in and fitted with an electric one.

The sash windows rattled in the January wind and the sitting room was as cold as a fridge, the grand-sized period furniture looked as old as the landlord himself. The kitchen was galley-sized and pokey; oil and grease on the stove top engrained from years of use, and I could see no oven to speak of. The landlord showed us the meter by the kitchen door, demonstrating with a fifty-pence piece how we could get electricity and heat.

Deirdre continued chatting away and I'd no idea what was being said. I looked at Grainne hoping my expression might reveal what I was thinking – no way in hell – the place was a health hazard. But she just looked around the sitting room, inspecting it, her face impassive and difficult to judge. At last we followed the landlord down the creaking staircase, and when he opened the door the cold winter air was a welcome antidote to the stink.

Deirdre smiled as she bid him goodbye.

*Slán*, she said, and as we passed through the gate and down the road she stopped and turned to me.

'I told him we'd take it.'

'Are you crazy? The place stinks like a fish yard,' and I immediately regretted my choice of words as Deirdre stared at me like an affronted schoolmarm.

'Well, as I said Michael,' and she stressed my name through gritted teeth, 'I didn't get any fish smell.'

'Well, what about the boiled cabbage pong, and the cat's piss? And did you not see your man's room when we walked down the stairs? Stacked ceiling high with old newspapers and god knows what else? If it weren't for the cats the place would probably be running wild with giant-sized rodents. I'd say he hasn't washed himself properly in half a century. He's like one of those old hill bachelors from a William Trevor story.'

'I don't know who the hell that is,' Deirdre said, 'but if you don't like it Grainne and me can find someone else.'

'Besides,' Grainne said quietly, smiling, 'you can't let us down now that you're our brother.'

'You told your man I was your brother? I knew it, I knew I heard the word *dearthair*. I'm not a complete eejit, you know.'

'He thought you were a boyfriend and said he didn't want that sort of thing going on under his roof, so I lied a little,' Deirdre said.

'Jesus,' I said.

'Would it be so bad being our brother?' Grainne asked, her green eyes sizing me up calmly. 'We'd have liked a brother, wouldn't we Deirdre?'

Deirdre didn't answer. At the end of the road she said that I needed to decide quickly because he'd only hold the flat for twenty-four hours.

I didn't want Grainne thinking badly of me, so we took the flat. When we moved in I sprayed air freshener all over the place, and with the sisters' incense going too, the place smelled like how I imagined a Buddhist temple might. The only thing that made it bearable was the odd day I might share breakfast with Grainne. I'd ask her about her plans or what she was reading, and she'd list off books and titles in Irish. I couldn't help wishing that I'd paid more attention to the language at school. But for the most part herself and Deirdre were long gone by the time I'd wake up, Grainne to lectures and Deirdre to Art College in town.

My heart was pounding like a kick drum when I opened the pub door. It was early enough for a Thursday night, but the place was already heaving, the air fogged with blue-grey cigarette smoke, and the odd trace of weed, as I pushed my way towards the bar. I looked through the crowd, and many a mad hairdo, until I saw a hand raised from the back of the pub, Grainne waving at me. I waved back.

The barmen moved between the beer pumps with seamless grace, filling up glasses of brown and black liquid, stopping to look at customers occasionally, their faces flushed, their expressions intent, nodding as I ordered a pint of Guinness. I spotted Seamus at the opposite end of the counter, his fingers stretched around three or four pints, a look of fierce concentration on his face as he slowly rotated and faced the thorny manoeuvre back through the throng.

Grainne smiled as I approached their table and invited me to sit next to her, and a gangly-looking fella in a rugby shirt with a white collar that was so vertical it looked as if it'd been starched. Seamus raised his eyebrows, his face half-obscured as he knocked back his drink. Grainne introduced me to a Roisin who greeted me in Irish, as did your man in the rugby shirt, Donal, and some other fella Sean, sitting next to Seamus, who also said *Dia dhuit*. It dawned on me then why Seamus hadn't asked me along knowing full well I'd be out of my depth. Roisin, realising my discomfort started speaking quietly in English.

'So, Michael you don't speak Irish then? Grainne said as much.'

'No, I don't. I can understand a little, but I couldn't speak it to save my life.'

'Grainne could teach you a bit. I'm sure she would if you asked,' she said, and she didn't take her eyes off me as she waited for my response.

She'd only to look at me and see how awkward I was, how I avoided her eye, to tell

I was stone mad about Grainne. Thank God Seamus interrupted and said something to her so that I could return to my pint and playing with the beer coaster.

Grainne and Donal were yapping away in Irish. As dumb as I was I could tell that Mr Starched Rugby shirt was some rich knob from south Dublin, from some rock like Foxrock or Blackrock. I could hear the raw spud in his mouth, the poker lodged up his arse from years at private boys' schools, the Irish that had the posh intonations of the privileged. I'd have sworn if I'd looked under the table he'd been wearing a pair of deck shoes, and if he'd ever been on a boat it was probably some yacht owned by Mummy and Daddy. He clearly fancied Grainne but I got the impression she wasn't that interested. I'd nearly finished my pint when he finally turned his attention to me, speaking in Irish.

'I don't speak Irish very well,' I replied.

'Oh, I'd just assumed,' he answered in English, and then paused before asking: 'But doesn't that make you feel less Irish, Michael?'

The table went quiet and all five faces, including Seamus who grinned wryly, and Grainne whose green eyes shone behind her black-framed glasses, looked at me, waiting for my answer. I stalled.

'How do you mean less Irish?'

'Well, it's our language and you don't speak it.'

'Most of the country don't speak it. Does that make them less Irish?'

'Well, it might,' he said.

'According to who?' I said. 'You or Irish speakers in general?' I tried to control my voice, but I wanted to punch the arrogant prick in the gob.

'Well, many Irish speakers feel that there should be more effort to encourage our nation to speak their language.'

'But what if it isn't their language? Hasn't been for hundreds of years? What would you do then? Force them to speak it like the English forced us to?'

'Well, it worked, didn't it?'

'Not altogether,' I said, 'or we wouldn't be having this conversation.'

'So, you don't feel less Irish?' he asked again.

'No, I don't. I was born and bred here. As far as I'm concerned that makes me as Irish as you believe yourself to be.'

'Interesting,' he said. He turned to Grainne and made some comment and I could tell she wasn't impressed. I downed my pint, said I'd an essay due and left.

I was in no mood for company, so I headed straight to my room, cursing the stiff door that never closed properly. Although it was still early for the night owl that I was in those days, I wished, not for the first time, that I hadn't left my essay until the last minute. We'd been reading The Dead and the question was something about stagnation, and how Joyce had portrayed this in his story. Years later, and away from Dublin for over half my life, I can still see myself so clearly in that room — chilled to the bone, heartsore and angry. I remember I didn't like Joyce's character Gabriel Conroy very much. He seemed like an arrogant fool who didn't know his wife Gretta at all, and it was likely she'd been longing for Michael Furey throughout their marriage. To be fair though, it would be hard for any man to compete with the romance of a broken-hearted ghost. I'd finished the introduction when there was a soft knock on my door.

'Sorry to disturb you Michael, but I've made a pot of tea if you'd like to have some?' Deirdre asked, popping her head behind the door.

I didn't really feel like it as I'd a long night ahead of me, but there was something about her expression that was so hopeful that I felt bad saying no.

The electric fire was on and she must have had it going for a while because for the first time ever, the room was lovely and warm.

'Weren't you going out with Grainne tonight?' she asked, pouring the tea, which to me looked and smelled nothing like tea, but some kind of strange, herbal infusion that only vegetarians drank.

'I've been and gone,' I said.

'You weren't out long.'

'I've an essay due tomorrow.'

'And who was down there? The Irish language lovers I suppose?'

'Yeah.'

She laughed. 'Did they deign to speak to you in English, Michael?

'They did, reluctantly.'

'I honestly don't know why Grainne hangs out with them. Your friend Seamus seems all right, but most of them are a bit up themselves.'

'So, you don't think I've to speak Irish to consider myself Irish?'

'What? Who said that?'

'Some fella called Donal.'

'I wouldn't mind him. He wouldn't know authentic Irish if it bit him on the arse.'

I laughed.

'So, how's the essay going?' she said, offering me a biscuit.

'I know what I need to write. I just have to get on with it now, you know.'

'God, I'm hopeless at all that stuff. Can barely write my own name, and I can't spell to save my life. That's why I love art so much.'

'Did you always want to be an artist?'

'Well, it was the only thing I was good at. I'm not the prized student like Grainne. And it was my only way of getting off the island.'

'So, you don't like the Aran Islands?'

'Ah, Inishmaan's all right, but I want to go to London, that's why I'm doing this foundation course and...'

She was in the middle of her sentence when suddenly the room was plunged into darkness, and the electric fire ticked, ticked and slowly fizzled out.

'That fucking meter,' I said, 'I'm convinced he has the thing rigged, you know.'

I got up and moved past Deirdre slowly in the dark, trying not to bump into a huge divan as I opened the door. I nearly broken my neck going down the few steps to the first landing. I put a fifty pence coin in, and the light came back on.

'It's a pity you've an essay to do Michael,' Deirdre said when I told her I'd better get back to it. She'd invited me to a gig in town, to meet some of her art college friends, adding, that none of them were very good at Irish.

'Well, maybe I should learn a bit more Deirdre,' I said.

'Not because of what Donal said?'

'No, but maybe I should give it a chance, you know. Maybe I dislike it because I was taught to.'

'Well, if you'd like me to help you, I'd be happy to teach you real west-coast Irish.'

'As opposed to the Irish we learn in Dublin?'

'Exactly,' she said, smiling.


At first, I thought it was the landlord's cats roaming the hall and stairs as they often did at night, but when I got up I saw that Grainne's bedroom door was slightly ajar. I stood on the landing, listening to the muffled sound of weeping. Perhaps she was crying in her sleep I thought, but when I turned back to my room, there was a long sigh and it sounded as if she was awake.

I knocked on her door gently, and whispered: 'Are you all right Grainne?'

'Yeah, I'm okay, I'm sorry to wake you. I'm just so cold. Come in if you like,' she said.

The room was dark except for three candles on the mantelpiece, their light quivering on the draughty walls.

'Here, sit down Michael,' she said and patted the side of the bed. She was dressed in a woolly Sherpa hat and jumper. She held her hand out.

'Jesus, you're freezing,' I said. 'Hang on a second and I'll get a blanket from my room.'

She smiled as I spread the blanket over her, asked me to sit on the bed again.

'That's lovely, thanks Michael.'

She looked different without her glasses, her eyes almond-shaped, her expression unguarded. I had to catch my breath.

'I'm sorry about tonight,' she said.

'Ah, don't worry about it.'

'Donal can be a bit of a prick,' she said.

'And how do you say that in Irish?'

She laughed, and her teeth flashed in the semi-darkness.

'You know Irish is very beautiful Michael. *Teach a chodlach Mícheál. Tá sé an fuar*, she said slowly, her expression as earnest as her tone.

'Something about sleep and the cold,' I said.

'*Tá.*'

Still speaking in Irish, she swept the blankets back and I think she told me to lie down, but I couldn't be sure. She took my hand again and drew me towards her so before I knew it I was lying next to her, and I could feel her warm breath on my ear. She must have heard my heart knocking inside my chest, like a late arrival who accidentally locks themselves out and thumps hard and insistent on a door.

'*Codlóimid Mícheál*,' she whispered. I was desperate to kiss her, but I was still so unsure of myself. She put her hand on my arm and turned me towards her, and then she kissed me.

'*Éisteacht leis an fharraige, Mícheál*,' she said as we undressed under the covers, and although I understood her, it wasn't until she fell asleep after that I knew what she'd really meant. On the wall opposite her bed was a large poster of the Atlantic Ocean. The sea grey, the waves white-tipped and wild. I wondered if this was how she got to sleep each night; imagining the sound of crashing waves breaking against her dreams, reminding her of home.

There was a hard frost expected that night, and part of me wanted to head out the back door as I'd often done at home in Drumcondra; watch the light brim slowly behind the nest of houses surrounding us, listen to the stillness of the morning interrupted by the cooing of pigeons, watch Venus fade, and the sky turn from a charcoal to a light blue. But if Grainne found me gone at four in the morning I thought she'd probably think I'd abandoned her, not to mention the landlord who might mistake me for a burglar and give me a whack over the head with a poker. Now that I think about it, I remember giving myself a good talking to then – how, there I was, sleeping next to Grainne Ní Cheallaigh, the girl I'd been dreaming about for weeks, and was I completely mad to be thinking of leaving her? So, I lay in bed, too excited to sleep and I thought about the people who'd lived in the house before us, and what other ghosts had looked out this window through the years, listening to the twittering of birds as the hours approached dawn. And one day I'd be a ghost myself, and someone else would look out, and maybe they'd wonder about the inhabitants of this house too.

At some point I must have nodded off. When I woke up, morning had crept through the small room, exposing the flawed walls, the uneven patches of cracked paint and mould lurking in corners. I lay as still as I could, my face basking in the cool sun, trying not to stir so I wouldn't wake Grainne. When she finally woke up she didn't smile or say good morning. She jumped out of bed and got dressed quickly. She looked around the room frantically, tossing clothes from her desk and chair onto the bed.

'Jesus, I can't find my alarm clock. What time is it do you think?'

'It's just after nine,' I said, looking at my watch.

'Fuck, I'll be late for my lecture.'

'Sure, what about it?' I said. 'It's no big deal if you miss the one, is it?'

'Maybe not for you Michael. Not all of us get everything handed to us on a plate.'

'Christ. What's that supposed to mean?'

'Nothing, it's just I've got to go. Please don't tell anyone about last night, will you? If Deirdre finds out, she'll kill me.

'Why would Deirdre care?'

'Ah, Christ, Michael, are you blind or pure stupid, or what?'

'What are you on about?'

'Never mind, I've got to go.'

She looked a right mess, her hair uncombed, her clothes a mish mash of colour, but I was so far gone on her she could have been wearing rags and I'd have thought she was gorgeous. I hopped out of the bed and followed behind her as she rushed out the door. And who should be standing on the landing but the landlord himself, and me in a T-shirt and boxers. My blood went cold.

He started barking at Grainne in Irish and again I heard that word I understood — *deartháir*. When he finally finished his rant, he turned his attention to me.

'You little blaggard,' he said in a croaky voice, like he was struggling to catch up with his wheezing breath, or his dentures had come loose.

'I rented you this flat on the proviso that you were a family. The small one, she told me you were a brother and two sisters. You can get out now, so you can, and you'd better hop it before I call the Guards, and have you arrested.

'Arrested for what?' I said to him.

'For incest.'

'But we're not related. You have it all wrong.'

'I see what I see with my own two eyes. Now pack your bags and get out. Get out, get out, or I'll call the guards.'

Grainne turned to me then. 'You better go Michael,' she said.

'I want you gone by lunch time, do you hear me?' the landlord shouted.

'I've got to go now,' Grainne said, and she slid past the old man and down the stairs, said *slán*, and I heard the door slam.

'Go on, off with you now you dirty so and so, and for God's sake get some clothes on. You're a disgrace,' he roared as he watched me return to my bedroom.

When I told Seamus what happened down the pub later, he nearly choked with laughter, spitting his beer all over his jumper like a sloppy toddler. And I suppose it was funny, looking back at it now, but I couldn't see it at the time. I'd been so shocked at Grainne, how she'd just left me there, that she'd said nothing to defend me. Well, maybe she had, but I couldn't understand a word.

'I just can't believe it,' I said to Seamus, as we demolished a packet of Tayto.

'Ah Mikey,' he said. 'I should have warned you about Grainne.'

'Warned me? How do you mean?'

'Well, she's beautiful and has brains to burn, but well, she's…'

'She's what?' I said mumbling as I tried to get one of the crisps stuck inside a molar out.

'Well, she's got a reputation. They call her an *banríon oighear*.'

'What the feck does that mean?'

'Jesus, you really are hopeless at Irish. It means the Ice Queen. Sure, she knocks around with private school boys from South Dublin, the likes that spend half the summer in an Irish language school, and the other half in the south of France, whose Daddies are politicians and judges and lawyers.'

'So?'

'Ah, Jesus, Michael, open your eyes. Sure, hasn't she been going out with Donal since first year.'

'What's she sleeping with me for then?' I asked, genuinely shocked.

'Beats me. You wouldn't be my type either, you know.'

'Ah, very funny, very droll. But seriously Seamus, she said she was cold, she was crying from the cold, you know. She was freezing. I felt her. As cold as marble.'

'See, what I mean, Michael, *an banríon oighear*.'

I often thought of Grainne Ní Cheallaigh over the years. The memory of her haunting me even after I emigrated to New Zealand when I was twenty-four. There was part of me naïve enough to think that if I willed it enough I might see her, even so far away. In winter I'd go walking in the snow-covered hills of Central Otago and wonder what had happened to that naïve young fella that was me, and what of Grainne, who I only saw one more time.

A fortnight after I was kicked out of the flat, Seamus called in home one night and said that he'd heard Deirdre had moved out, and that the sisters weren't talking to each other because of what had happened. When I told him I was surprised, that I'd thought they were really close, he rolled his eyes.

'Jesus, Michael. Sometimes you're really thick.'

'How do you mean?'

'Everyone knows Deirdre was mad about you.'

'I hadn't a clue. She never let on to me.'

'Like you would have noticed, anyway,' he said.

He was right of course. I didn't notice, and I was glad I hadn't told him or anyone that I'd gone back to Ranelagh a few nights after I'd packed my bags. I'd wanted to talk to Grainne. I hadn't a clue what I would have said to her. I'd hardly slept or eaten since I'd left, and it was all I could do to stop myself going mad. I remember that evening especially tonight, because it was snowing then too.

I left Drumcondra after dinner and I headed out into the city. Past the icy black gates and steps of old Georgian tenement flats on Parnell Street, the raw smell of alcohol and cigarettes as pub doors opened and closed on Lower O'Connell Street, past emaciated junkies clutching paper cups begging on O'Connell bridge, up Westmoreland and past the dimmed lights of Bewleys, past Trinity College, and through the crowds on Grafton Street making their way home. I skirted the edges of Stephen's Green. On and on I walked, getting warmer as I went, the snow falling softly, beautiful and light, and dream-like. By the time I got to Ranelagh my head and coat were soaked through. I was only a few minutes from the flat when I saw Grainne and Donal walking in the village. I hid behind a tree and watched them. She was dressed in her Sherpa hat and a long woollen coat. She was laughing as she let go of his hand and began to swirl like a dervish in the snow. He took her hand again then and they crossed the road, and out of sight. As I stood there, my soul swooned. I watched the snow falling through the air softly and onto the street. After a few minutes I walked on.

# 55

## Immanuel Mifsud

### Translated by Ruth Ward

This is one of Silvio's most annoying habits: everywhere he goes he's always very early. Even though he doesn't like his work, he's always early. Wherever he goes, whenever he goes, he's always early. Then he never knows what to do until it's time. Lately he goes nowhere except to work: from home to work, from work back home. Then, once a week, he does the shopping. He gets home and watches some movie, some program he doesn't enjoy, some documentary on revolting insects, some variety show. Well, he no longer watches variety shows, because they don't do those anymore. Sometimes he watches programs he's already seen twice, and lately he's even started watching the teleshopping channel.

Silvio is fifty-five.

Two years ago, his wife left him. Suddenly. She'd been telling him that there was nothing more between them, but Silvio never really thought she would leave him. He always thought that she loved him enough to stick with him, despite there being nothing left between them. But she left. Since then, they've never spoken, except once when she phoned him on Christmas. By the next Christmas this tradition had stopped.

Silvio is fifty-five but he feels much older. At work, where he's been employed for over thirty years, he's had enough. He's seen many colleagues come and go. No one has hung on but him. Not because he's happy there but now, at fifty-five, it's very difficult to find another job. Not to mention that after all these years, there's no other job he can do. His job displeases him and he's sad there. The only moment when he's not put-out is when Mandy, the cleaner, comes to clean his office. He keeps looking at her, at her long and brightly colored nails, at her hair pulled back, at the butterfly she has tattooed on her right ankle and the lizard tattooed on her left one. He always imagines it coming to life and creeping up to where he can't see—under her skirt, beneath the stained uniform which fits her so tightly. It's not the first time that Mandy has caught him looking at her with that gaze that men of a certain age cast. Whenever she spots him doing it, she gives him a little smile:

— You ok, Mr. Carabott?

Silvio Carabott is fifty-five. Mandy the cleaner is twenty-two. Her mobile rings very often; sometimes she answers, sometimes she doesn't, depending on who's calling.

— How was your weekend, Mr. Carabott?
— Not bad.
— Maybe you went out to some nightclub, Mr. Carabott?

Nightclub? Maybe Mandy knows what has happened to him? Why does she imagine he spends the weekend nightclubbing and not, as men of his age should, with his wife and children and grandchildren?

— Nah, didn't feel like that this weekend.
— Yeah, I know. Sometimes you just don't feel like it. But you do need to enjoy yourself a little, no?
— How did you spend yours, Mandy? With your boyfriend?
— Boyfriend? No, Mr. Carabott, I'm still alone.

It's almost at the tip of his tongue: alone? A chick like you?!

— I'm not kidding you, Mr. Carabott. It's still too early to go steady with anyone. Later on, we'll see. But you know what, Mr. Carabott? I'm doing fine as I am because I do as I please and go wherever and with whomever I want. For New Year's I'm going skiing. Just look at my friends, those who are in some relationship; they're always stuck under their boyfriend. Nah, not for me. How boring! Why would I need a boyfriend?

But Silvio's mind has already gone in a different direction: what if this Mandy is one of those? Lately there seems to be so many of them, especially now that they can even marry. You can't be sure of anyone. After all, those were the rumors about Miriam, his ex-wife. Word has it that she's often seen with this big woman with her hair half-long, half-shaven. It's said that they're seen together on Saturday nights. And some are even saying they bought a flat together. Silvio doesn't know who's spreading these rumors, and he doesn't even recall how he first got wind of them, but he knows what's going around. Every day he hears these rumors, even when he lies down and closes his eyes after a half-marathon of televiewing. Strange how in almost thirty years of marriage he never noticed anything. She never said anything; never even dropped a hint. Nothing. And he never noticed. There was a time, on the contrary, when he started suspecting that Miriam had set her eyes on the husband of a friend they knew well and used to go out with frequently, together with other couples. He started brooding over this a lot until one day, on an evening near Christmas, this friend came over without her husband and announced that he had left her for a much younger woman. On that day Silvio concluded that even if he'd had good reason to suspect his wife and the friend's husband, he could now put his mind to rest, and he had a very good Christmas indeed. That's what that guy did: he met a young girl and he left. A much younger girl. Maybe Mandy's age.

— Must get on with my work, Mr. Carabott. If you need anything, just ask me. I don't know, maybe you need me to go shopping for you, because you're all the time stuck at your desk working, my goodness!

Mandy. God forbid she's one of those. What a waste that would be! Lately there are many such cases. Take Dr. Camenzuli's daughter, for instance. She's one of those. You wouldn't believe it, a girl with a face like that—and then she goes to waste in that manner. This blessed Mandy, though, thank goodness she's around to break the monotony of a long day chained to this desk.

Today, as always, he's arrived early. He's ventured into the city to watch a film. He hasn't been to the cinema in ages. Can't even recall the last time he went. Must have been with Miriam though. He doesn't like the cinema, and he used to beg his ex-wife not to have to go whenever she wanted to drag him to some film. The darkness in the theater bugs him… and the sound of people crunching their popcorn and slurping on their soft drinks; and the never-ending ads before the film starts; and the people who make you get up from your seat because they came late or because they want to go buy something during the intermission; and that pushing during the entrance and the exit… everything! Moreover, he was never very much interested in films and lately he's liking them even less, so much so that he almost prefers the teleshopping programs to them. But this morning, as soon as he got up, he made the decision to go out and watch a film that evening, and then pick up a pizza and eat it while watching television. There's a need for big, radical change in life. If the country has changed so much, why not his life, too? As he started his car, it occurred to him that he should get a new one; and he should go out at least on Saturdays—to some nightclub as Mandy suggested; and on Sundays he should go to the stadium to watch some match; and he might as well go to the club, too, now that his political party is doing so well.

An hour and a half to the start of *Bohemian Rhapsody*. She's wearing a summer dress: light blue with little pink and yellow flowers. Flat sandals. Her toenails are perfectly pedicured. The sunglasses rest on her head. She sits on a bench, looking at a dead fountain in the middle of the square. She lights up a cigarette. She wears only one ring, on the righthand pinky. She places the cigarette between her unpainted lips, flashing a dainty ring in the shape of a heart with a little red stone in the center. There's more than an hour left before the film starts. Her hair is the color of hazelnut. Some distance away, a touristy couple ambles about, sunburned. In this square Silvio Carabott had met Miriam. That's why he's come here, to think of her. He still hasn't accepted the fact that she's no longer his wife. Sometimes he's on the verge of phoning her but he's afraid that she'd just hang up, or she wouldn't answer... or someone else might answer instead. He fears hurt. So he never calls. This is where they had met. Possibly in this very corner. She was with a friend of hers, and he was alone. She and her friend were going to the cinema, and he was going to that woman who used to wait for him at her front door. He didn't use to go to her frequently, but sometimes he just had to. And on that day, on his way to that woman, he saw these two girls, and one of them—out of the blue—looked at him and smiled. And he kept walking after them, and even went to the cinema and sat right behind them. During the intermission one of the girls went out and the other, the one who had smiled at him, turned and asked him if he liked the film. He replied no and added that she was very attractive. The next day they were strolling about the streets of that same city, like two happy souls, and at one point he reached for her hand, and they walked hand in hand for the rest of the evening. The woman who was waiting for him at the doorstep waited in vain until she grew old, called it a day, and her street became unrecognizable: no one waits on doorsteps anymore or loiters in the street except eager waiters holding menus, soliciting passersby to step into their restaurant.

— Hello, are you Maltese?

He gets alarmed and then realizes that the color of her eyes matches that of her hair. Those eyes look at him and say nothing, but at the same time, seem to be expecting him to say a lot.

— Yes, I am. Sorry, I didn't realize you were talking to me.

— How come? You haven't stopped eyeballing me since you got here.

— Is that so?

— Oh, you haven't noticed that either?

— Sorry, didn't mean to harass you or anything.

— Harass me? Oh, I'm not the uptight type that have become trendy of late. I'm of my own age. And in my time, we weren't so delicate.

— True. Nowadays you can't even look at anyone.

— Well, you'll never be mistaken for contemporary—because you've surely been gazing at me.

— Hmm, I don't know what to say really. I'm sorry.

— Wouldn't it be better if you just told me why you're looking at me?

— Just... sorry... I didn't mean to bother you.

— Who said you are? Marika.

— Pardon?

— That's me. I'm Marika. My name's Marika.

— Right.

— Do you have a name?

— Yes, sure.

— So? Will you tell me?

— Silvio.

— So why were you looking at me?

— I honestly didn't notice I was.

— Oh, I see. I thought you liked me.

— Never said I didn't.

— Ah, so you *were* looking. Come. You can sit by me if you'd like. You have my permission.

— Thank you.

Now it's not just her eyes that penetrate him but even the fragrance exuding from her body. Drawing closer now, he can see the creases around her eyes; and when she takes a whiff of her cigarette, there are more creases around her mouth.

— Marika, did you say? Do you like this square?

— I've seen nicer, but it's alright. This square is where I first met my husband, so inevitably I think of him.

— My, what a coincidence! This is where I met my wife. And if I'm not mistaken, it was at this very corner.

— Ah, so you're married.

— Was.

The kissing is good. Or let's say, her kissing is. He hadn't had a taste of someone else's mouth for a long time. Years. So as soon as she slipped off her sandals and sat next to him, turning towards him, he knew that in the next moment he'd be tasting her mouth. The kissing is good. The taste of mint after she brushed her teeth to get rid of the tobacco taste is good. And the fragrance on her neck that's getting stronger, is good too. By now *Bohemian Rhapsody* has finished. Maybe the last show has started or is about to. He's still got the ticket in his back pocket.

— Would you rather I switched off the light?
— It's okay. As you wish.
— Maybe you're just a bit... shy.
— I'm not, but maybe you are.
— Didn't you say you liked me, when we were having pizza?
— Yes, very much so.

He can't understand. Fifty-five is not old. He's not young like he was when he'd met his ex-wife, still, being fifty-five doesn't make you old. And she's attractive: her hair, her eyes, her shape. Even her voice is pleasant, especially when she speaks quietly and when she laughs. He found her pretty even when she put her cigarette to her mouth, in spite of his dislike of smoking. Fifty-five is not that old an age. And yet... despite everything... even though she's... how to say it?... even though this woman is fine, fabulous even... well at fifty-five you're not some grandpa, are you? Exploring her mouth and discovering the sweetness, he'd thought his moment of glory had finally arrived, the moment to vindicate all that had happened with Miriam. He'd noticed that he'd never thought of Miriam as much as he was thinking of her tonight. He'd almost wished she were there—seeing him, seeing them on the couch, watching them rise all excited, making their way towards the innermost room where he never dreamed he would go. He'd wished she was there, watching in some corner... incensed. He knew Miriam, knew that she would never have imagined that he could ever manage to... fifty-five is just not that old. Maybe in the old days it was a venerable age but nowadays at fifty-five you still have ten more years in employment. So, little by little, they set out to complete the moment... when it became evident that the moment wouldn't even be starting, Silvio took a deep breath and exhaled. She stood looking at nothing for a while and then, as a kind of conclusion, lit up a cigarette. Thank god Miriam is not around. Thank god for that.

— So, do you think we could get together again?
— Wait a minute, let me grab an ashtray.

She went out of the room and he was quick to look at himself—a little boy opening his exercise book to find out he got all his answers wrong. Despite the half-darkness that had settled over the room as she'd drawn the flowered curtains, he could still see all his mistakes:  a long series of them or, better said, one big one. She returned balancing an ashtray in one hand and her mobile in the other. Also, she got dressed, a light top and Bermudas. Once he saw her dressed, he reflexively pulled the sheet over himself.

— So?
— What?
— I asked you something.
— You asked…?
— If we could get together again.
— Ah, yes… yes, why not.
— You want to?
— Yes, why not. If you want.
— Of course, I do. But do you?
— Yes. We'll do that.
— When? Tomorrow?
— Tomorrow? I have to see if I have something tomorrow. Take my number and send me a message on WhatsApp in the afternoon. Coffee? I'm going to brew some. In the meantime, you can keep me company in the kitchen or make yourself comfortable on the sofa. Or maybe you don't have coffee this late? Maybe you won't be able to sleep if you do.
— What time is it?
— Almost midnight, I believe.

Three-thirty and he still can't sleep, because he still can't believe it. Even those nights when he used come home early, say at ten instead of the usual well past midnight, on his way to his room he used to feel so embarrassed at his parents. His father was the same age at that time as he is now, and his father's exercise book obviously contained no errors. And he can't make sense of it because sometimes when he is in bed—alone—and right beside him appears Mandy out of thin air, in the same uniform she'll be wearing in the morning, with her hair a little tousled or when, sometimes, she appears already undressed, it's a different story altogether. Two years of sitting around watching television alone and today, on a whim, instead of going to the cinema, he'd ended up in the apartment of this Marika … who'd attracted him in the same corner of the square where he had first met Miriam. Marika gave him her number so they could meet again. It's twenty to four. He's not going to phone now of course. He closes his eyes again, hoping to fall asleep. She rode down in the lift with him and when they got to the front door, he turned to her, planning to kiss her.

– Look, I'm sorry.
– What for?
– Well… you know.
– Don't worry, sometimes it just happens.
– It never happened to me.
– Next time might be different. You'd better get going. I don't want us to be seen by some neighbor.
– Shall I message you tomorrow?
– You can.

Two hours and ten minutes have passed since he sent her a second message. So far, he hasn't received an answer.

## ORATORY
Paddy Bushe

It's your oratory, said an archaeologist friend
About the high ridge and pointed-arch gables
On the brand-new polycarbonate greenhouse

That was our coronavirus summer project.
And yes, you could see a silhouetted echo:
Gallarus, say, or Cill Ó Buaine. We laughed.

Later, as I barrowed clay into raised beds,
Sunlight, as it was prismed into the interior,
Miracled a crystal edifice, illuminated a *Vita*

That might have been lived in saintlier times
When work and prayer in unison conspired
Against the plagues decreed by God or man.

Now our seedling spring onions are uncoiling
Their bowed heads from the clay. Salad leaves
Are raising themselves to embrace the light,

And I have planted garlic to overwinter here,
Placed each clove deep and firm to guard
Against the dark and purify the blood in spring.

True, our oratory runs from north to south
And not from Christ's risen sun to its setting.
But heaven knows we had lost track of that axis

Years before we knew its orientation. So now,
Along our raised beds, *laboremus* at our ease,
*Oremus* in our own words, *et nil timeamus.*

VESPERS
Ger Duffy

*(Luke 7:37-38)*

In the house of the Pharisees the men
speak of taxes, drought, miracles.
I bring wine, bread, olives. They say
only men leave their families for you.
Sweat beads your forehead, trickles
inside my robe, your eyes impale me,
riddling my thoughts. My bracelets
tremble before you. Breaking the jar
of nard, I kneel, my tears tracing tracks
on your dusky feet. Cupping your cracked
sole, I press in oil scented valerian.
My long hair hides my lips curling
over your square toes- tasting desert dirt,
salt, sweat. Yet you yield to my touch.
Your hand hovers above my head,
my thumb circling your heel, my hair
caressing your feet, killing all talk.

## THE MAGI'S CAMEL
Daniel Hinds

*'With the voices singing in our ears'*
*— T. S. Eliot, Journey of the Magi*

The fat god squats between back braes.

Does not discern the soft gasp as hoof meets grit;
Even the dust fears the determined, unerring hammer

Of two dark nails.

The murmur of cloth, creaking leather and dry lips,
The gold of a weak winter's sun, a thin wash for a parched place.
The sense behind, of a conversation on direction spoken frank.

This is a life with few gifts; noses closed to scent,
Thick lashes shading even the season's poor wealth.
The murder of your bones by flights of carrion birds.

The shaggy and silken fortress moves,
Gains and loses territory with every step.
Stamps the sand with an alien sigil.

A creature with six hands; two to bear the whip,
Four to do the work. The adoration of the magi is a tough love.

The way always, of those of the hill
And those who speak from the mount.

Slick guts work the miracle;
A drop will last a week.

A drink lasts longest for those last to drink.

Only the sight of a horse without rider, white and old as starlight,
Running masterless among long grasses, cooled and stilled by night,
Stirs the hard muscle of a young heart from its dry and steady beat.

The blurred and furry pulpit makes its way across the desert.
Magicians preach from the turret, but none here will follow the hard way.
For all they say, only thick soles and spindle limbs know the hardness.

They know the weight of all the far travelled books of sorcery.
The washerwomen and shepherds jeer, fling earth;
They have their own magic to work.

Yes, three kings, three trees, a star, a child,
But two humps.

Discarded crowns gain swift burial in the desert.
No, the way back the same as the way there.

AIRMID
Niamh Twomey

Wrapped up soft as willow like the day you were born,
they lower you into a tilled grave.
Night falls heavy on my shoulders.

I stay by your side
as winter leaves cling to their branches.
*Remember, Brother, how I taught you*

*to hang Chamomile from rafters,*
*to swim in the Boyne, shape animals from clouds;*
*rubbed docks on your nettle-flecked skin.*

*How we dived for Carrageen from the seafloor,*
*scoured marshlands for Silverweed, forests for Wild Garlic,*
*steeped Arnica for the bruises of warriors.*

Rhododendron descends from Siberian mountains,
Peels of Peruvian Bark fall in my feverous lap.
Euphrasia clears my eyes, Plantago cleanses my ears,

Calendula, Wolf's-bane, Red Onion, Yellow Broom,
Figs land at my feet, oozing treacle, Nettles to be stewed,
Chickweed, Elderflower; Myrtle stars the dark.

Your grave offers up these docks to be rubbed on the sting of it.
Bramble and Nightshade creep through the hedgerow,
an elixir folding into the wounds of the world.

I think I will never rise but your voice is blooming in the dawn light;
*Look, sister, at the fruit of us.*
*Look to all that we have planted*
                              — *harvest it.*

# Two Poems
## Kate McHugh

---

GREEN SETTEE

*Green is warm,* she would say,
Lips pinched to my perch on the carpet,
Her mind on pea soup for December breakfast,
Moss mumbling sleep under windowsills of snow,
The evergreens of her garden grinding teeth to the wind.

But the night of her wake, in the room of red carpet,
That green settee sat bare and untouched
By the line of mourners long standing.
And rising from the coffin she could see
*Green is grass dew on the mornings of country misery.*

# WALK OF THE DEAD

*In memory of Ann Newton*

In the dawning day's hush of Hallows' Eve
She lies silent in sleep with a last breath,
And that night, with children dressed to deceive,
She paces the portalled pathway of death.
Her faint footsteps follow young door to door,
And as they sing, chant, demand something sweet,
She prays under the swaying sycamore,
Standing cold, searching a foregone heartbeat.
Up above descend wet whispers of rain,
Tears of family crying for her soul,
The swelling first song in their house of pain,
A circle of scattered grief in windows.
Looking within, she sees her daughter's light,
But she, looking out, sees only the night.

# THE SCATTERING
Graham Allen

*For Kevin Griffin, 25 October 2020, Rossbeigh Beach*

Words cannot tell the loss of him,
no clock face or set of numbers can count,
there is no map can navigate our mourning,
save the old, mythic songs he sometimes taught.

We scattered his ashes where Niamh and Oisín
passed over into the land of Tir na nÓg,
and where that same Oisín, unaged,
returned to converse with Patrick and his God.

A sudden, thin, beginning of a rainbow,
pointed the way as the waves broke on rocks
that tumbled back into the ocean's embrace
and left us unfooted, a shepherdless flock.

Beached like dolphins far from their homes,
we searched for more signs of the land of the young,
but all I had for comfort was Corinthians and love
and Shelley's lines on the Many and the One.

We live our lives as wanderers,
under alien rain and an alien sun,
but here I begin to understand a little,
what made this man stay and what made him run.

## FUNERAL GAMES
Bernadette Gallagher

*After the burial of Patroclus*

After I am buried
let the celebrations begin.

Instead of a chariot race
walk in the forest, where
Jack's field used to be.

In place of a fist fight
a gentle run on the sands
of *Harbour View.*

Instead of a wrestling match
a swim after the run.

In place of a quarter mile sprint
a drink at *The Pink Elephant.*

Instead of a fight in full armour
a walk up *Mullaghanish.*

In place of throwing a meteorite
a cycle up the *Windy Gap.*

Instead of hitting a dove
a walk, above *Dispensary Cross*
to look north, south, east, and west.

In place of throwing a spear
stand in our forest and listen.

## MY EYES
Dermot Bolger

My eyes weren't lying in wait when you chanced on them

At the padlocked gates of a Protestant church, so remote

That interments rarely discommode the slanting headstones


Or moss-choked gravel where I parked, invisible to anyone

Until they rounded the bend of that narrow country lane

Where I waited to collect a hiker after her Sunday walk.


I didn't know of your bolthole cottage beyond the church,

With surveillance cameras arrayed on its fortified gates,

Where you retreated to brood on dead friends to avenge


And who might double-cross you with drugs shipments.

I was unaware of your identity when we came face to face

After you braked hard taking that bend, spying me there.


The chilling coldness with which your eyes scrutinised mine,

Calculating risk, evaluating dangers to which I was oblivious,

Thinking you were just a big swinging dick young executive


Annoyed to find someone occupying a favoured parking space.

Revving your engine, you passed with a contemptuous glance,

Dismissing me as being too inconsequential to pose a threat.

Two weeks later, I recalled your gaze, watching news footage

Of that church cordoned off, your windscreen shattered,

An assassin's car burnt out in the spot where I had parked.


When I wake some nights I wondering if, taken by surprise

By a waiting car, your final thoughts were a fervent prayer

To glimpse me there, a saviour with inconsequential eyes.

CATHODE RAYS
Patrick Chapman

The woman on the white park bench
opens a broadsheet to save herself
from seeing the man closing in.
And you, clever boy, you absorb
it all, sensing the shock in her
eyes as the car-coated, kid-
gloved hitman raises his gun
and shoots her right between
the three-day week and the IRA.
The paper falls away. Her body
slumps. You never shake the image,
even after forty years.

Now you turn the lantern on
only to look for her there;
or the massacre on Gauda Prime;
or Caligula ripping the foetus
out of Drusilla; or Hettie helping
Bernard stop the harvest —
but all you pick up
are footprints in snow.

A slow bomb went off.

Your memory failed

to see that it needed

a regun.

## The Old Fort in Agra
William Doreski

Politics has soured our breath
and rendered us ungrammatical.
The light on the snow this morning
looks tainted with colonies
of the most willful bacteria—
those that plunder us organ
by organ until we withdraw
in ashes, grease, and rubble.

You think that peculiar blue
looks less nasty than the bruises
welling around the cat-bites
you receive every night from
our self-tormented Siamese.
You believe that each day offers
the same set of rusty old tools,
although requiring fresh repairs.

But I spot something I glimpsed
at sunrise in Agra, the old fort
steaming with damp and sorrow.
An effect too subtle to photograph
but a brief, distinct undertone
that could trigger unruly mobs
like those swarming the capitol
four days before my birthday.

You don't see how the pieces
of the puzzle fit. They don't:
that's the point. Note the tracks
of an abandoned pet browsing
up to our front door, retreating
with a lingering sigh. One of us
should stay up all night to lure
this lost creature to safety.

You doubt that any life-form
is safe in this stressed climate
with its hundred-year storms
occurring weekly. Yes, the bleached
horizons have warped, but cries
of hunger coiling around us
as we sleep will sour dreams
that otherwise might solve us.

## PLUMS
V.P. Loggins

When I returned home from military service
      where I was taught to kill
and, among other things, to make my bed
with corners stretched, tucked, and buried
so that the blanket and the sheet beneath it
were as tight as a trampoline, a coin used
by the sergeant to try their tension, a taut
mirror to the state of my tested nerves,
I began to make my soldier's bed at home,
having learned these morning imperatives,
with the same diligence as in the barracks,
where such things were expected of you,
and where my training in the arts of death
and dying would never be forgotten.
                        One day
my father captured me as I was leaving
the house and said, "Why not let your mother
do a few things for you?" And though
he knew that things had changed for me
they had not changed for her.
                    Next morning
I departed with my bed a holy wreck,
and when I returned the room and covers
of the bed were as they had always been
when my mother set all domestic things
as straight as the march I used to think was life.
That morning it was as if nothing important
had ever happened though, despite appearances,
everything had, for all things with me
had been turning, as plums ripening on
the tree my father had planted in our yard
         were turning
in the silent insistence of September's sun,
soon to be picked or forever ruined.

## SEPTEMBER 13, 2001
Dante Micheaux

I watched them fall, jump into smoke,
saw some mount the sky with invisible wings.
I stood in the avenue and fell to my knees
as the sentinels melted into the earth.
I can still smell the burning.

But that is not today. Today the movies are free.

The cinema is filled: seats, aisles, stairs—
defying fire codes, the vengeful roar
of fighter planes above.

Today we are more a country because we suffered
together, clear mourning, and now the movies are free.

One after the other, after the other, after the other,
after the other: we consume the narcotic
on the big screen. *Forget your troubles. C'mon, get happy.*
*C'mon and chase your cares away.* We laugh and cry
for the day before yesterday as dust settles
on the buildings that were spared.

I breathed the dead. The dead are in me.
I cast them out and breathed them in again.

But that is not today, when pederasts and gunslingers
compete for my attention. They all lose
to the blind seamstress and her son.

In the happy dark, all votes are casts for the fool,
the greasy jester with funny talk and slow response,
shifty eyes and stunted intellect.

He has a plan like the gunslingers on screen.
*Smoke 'em out!* And we don't care because the movies
are free—*as free as the wind blows* the remains of the dead

through the streets where fraternity has sprung:
men and women smiling, with the ashes
of some investment banker staining teeth,
the last whisper of a secretary caught in the lungs.

We trade the world to be number one
—mother of exiles whom we have exiled.

The fingers that groped the sky have become leprous
and fallen away from the hand that fed them poison
in exchange for the gold kept buried in the belly of the city.

But that is not today when the movies are free—the cinema,
the orgy of escape, our eyes glossing over. We will die
before we love one another.

The credits are rolling but the enemy is not in here.

WELCOME TO SHOW BUSINESS
Manuel Igrejas

"Dorothy Malone is sitting in her hotel room with nothing to do!"
The urgent male voice belonged to the director of the film festival we repped.
I was alone in the midtown Manhattan office of a small publicity firm.
New at the job, I was baffled. I never expected to hear those words.
My previous job, driving a recycling truck, hadn't prepared me
For entertaining an Oscar-winning actress.
I took the message and left it on the desk of my boss,
A burly and famously nasty press agent. She was almost six feet tall
And terrifying in her purple cowboy boots.
I did my assignments while I waited for her to return,
Typed my puppy dog versions of press releases and tried to make them punchy;
It helped that I thought of them as poems, poems about shows.
This was 1981, before computers, and I worked on a twitchy electric typewriter
That my big hands, used to manual labor, pounded senseless.
I wasn't a good typist and kept a gallon of White Out
With a pump dispenser on my desk.

As I typed and pumped I wondered if I should rush to the Hotel Pierre
And keep Dorothy company until one of her movie star friends showed up.
I wasn't sure if I was allowed to leave the office
Or if I had the resources to entertain Ms. Malone.
What did I know about her? She was blonde and beautiful and
She had won an Oscar for *Written on the Wind.*
An actress friend used her as an example to describe *indicating*
"She always shows you how hard she's working."

Maybe. But I remember her from *The Big Sleep*
When Bogart's Sam Spade ducks into the Acme Book Store.
Dorothy is a tall girl with a full face, dark hair pulled back,
Owlish glasses framing her big, insouciant eyes.
While Bogart tosses some rare book mumbo jumbo at her
She sizes him up and artfully wields a pencil
As a potential deadly weapon or love token. He's impressed,
She's impressed and he decides to wait out the rain in her company.
"I've got a bottle of pretty good rye," he says and she has paper cups.
His raised brow indicates her glasses. She removes them,
Then undoes her hair, letting it cascade around her lovely, alert face.
"It looks like we're closed for the afternoon," she says.

*That* self-possessed woman is sitting alone in her room,
With nothing to do?
Could someone that famous and accomplished feel
As frightened and desolate as I did?

Then my boss clomped in, a mink coat over her jeans and cowboy boots.
She settled behind her desk, went over her messages.
"What the fuck is this?" She waved the Dorothy Malone message at me
Her gimlet eyes scanned me as if I were the one who dared to be in distress.
She read the message aloud:
"Dorothy Malone is sitting in her hotel room with nothing to do."
Then she added her official response "Fuck her!"

The next day the festival was cancelled and its director
Skipped town without paying any of his bills. Welcome to Show Business.
But, for a moment, I was tenuously connected to a beautiful movie star
And we were two lonely people confined to our separate cubicles.

## ANNE SEXTON IN GALWAY
Orla Fay

*1996 - 1998*

In that confessional autumn and winter
the Atlantic kicked the leaves up Newcastle
and Thomas Hynes Road until they lay
limply in the gutters, defeated dogs.

I wondered what would become of me,
so ghostlike as I walked past the college
walls with my backpack heavy and comforting
unlike the leaden ball that sought to calibrate

itself between my stomach and throat
always just grazing the heart.
Tasked with presenting an assignment on
Sexton and Plath in a tutorial,

encouraged momentarily by the visiting lecturer,
an American woman, what did I know of 'Her Kind'?
Yet, I knew of fairy-tales and nursery rhymes,
of witches and defiant women like Lady Godiva!

I knew about shame and embarrassment,
of things I whispered to myself in the dark.
Sylvia was another matter. I took her to Salthill
and embraced her stubbornness

in the face of the saving grace of ocean.
Its tidal reminder proffered a bigger picture,
soothed those burning questions, those licking flames:
Who am I? What am I doing here? Where do I belong?

I had forgotten that the city stretched beneath one night,
shimmering yellow, orange, and red from an eyrie.
More beautiful than hell, stars scorched pale faces
in rites of passage that would be the future tattooed.

FREDERICK DOUGLASS ABOARD A SONNET
Kimberly Reyes

I don't know at which port he stood, what oar,
heard, inhaling mist—& this saline film

reel, splicing to a Point of No Return:

                    a clarity,         a shuffling about decks.

                    What's stolen for Van Diemen's Land, Charleston?
                    What of asylum granted, hope harbored

with abandonment? The same pastel gale

& silent boats, still frames in Cobh, Cape Coast

& familial fetters boring tide, bloat,

lighting channels, every port rang, calling
steadfast incitement (!)—Boston, Liverpool
once faith & Mersey met the Irish Sea

what wonder could be felt abreast green sails
raised in insight, heeding every crew's caws.

PROUST'S ASTHMA
Jake Crist

Those dark years, not writing, confined to bed,
I would often imagine him chauffeured
In a sealed car through the Bois de Boulogne
To be among the blossoming hawthorns,

At a late hour when the chestnut pollen
Has fallen dormant and the day's upthrown
Dust has settled, still dogged by the pervasive
Chill, against which he's fortified himself

With manifold mufflers, three overcoats
Thrown over a thermogene-padded suit,
A swathe of woolen sweaters, a cravat
Of smoke from an Espic cigarette;

And then, after this rare sortie outside,
I would, in bed, see him in his brass bed
Tarnished by fumigations of Escouflaire,
And with his notebook and pen, lying there

In the cork-lined room with heavy curtains,
Resume his sanction on suffocation:
A deep draft—Combray, madeleine, *Maman*—
Welcoming the mercy of each comma.

## THE PRIME OF MISS JEAN BRODIE
Fiona B. Smith

*The Prime of Miss Jean Brodie*
was what I was reading that day.
The crème de la crème girls
giggled their way into my August
head as the lake shimmered,
a migraine just above my eyes.
I blocked it out, kept it all at bay.
The burrs of Edinburgh in my head
kept me safe with Jean and the girls
in that faded bedroom with its wardrobe
of walnut, the much-used mirror mottled.
I was surprised I was left there that long,
reading on my bed in the close afternoon.
It must have been hours – I finished the book –
Nobody came to check up on me,
call me outside as it was *such a lovely day.*
Later I was angry with Miss Brodie.
I could never look at her again.
She had kept me unknowing, trapped
In her garamond straitjacket of snobbery,
Morningside cardigans, rigidity, mockery.
While outside there was dying.
The lake shone whitely, meanly in the sunlight.
Not even the buzz of an insect shut inside
broke the silence of that long afternoon.
I clung to Miss Brodie in the haze.
I could ignore the whispers in my head
until they eventually came to tell me,
the 11-year-old sister with a book.

# In Your Bones
## Lydia Searle

---

*'Your beliefs will be the light by which you see, but they will not be what you see and they will not be a substitute for seeing.'*
— Flannery O'Connor, *Mystery and Manners*

Growing up with an Irish mother I was taken to church weekly. She's the sort of
Protestant that carries a stone in her pocket to remind her to pray for the healing of
Ireland. God was always there in our house but He was loving, not the sort I read about
in *Angela's Ashes*. He was also the God that knew when I did things like hugged that kitten
so hard it was sick everywhere or placed a row of slugs on the patio heater and watched as
they sizzled slowly into dark crisps.

At church, we sang songs in a draughty hall, 'If I were a butterfly I'd thank you Lord for
giving me wings' and 'Shine, Jesus, Shine.' The church sat in the middle of a council estate.
In summer we played out back, careful not to step on any used needles or broken glass.
There would be extra chairs laid out at lunch for those who had nowhere to go, recovering
alcoholics, lonely older people nobody invited for lunch. The foster kids of my Mum's
friend would be there. One of them, Mark, sat next to me in Maths at school. He would
turn his eyelids inside out when the teacher wasn't looking and tell me it was permanent.
My mother said he hadn't had an easy life and I was to be kind to him and I wondered
where this infinite kindness in my mother came from.

Years later at University, my poetry professor said, 'Obviously nobody believes in God
anymore.' A girl beside me with a nose ring and half her head shaved nodded.
'God is a patriarchal construct,' she whispered. I nodded, pretending to write things down.
Believing in God was childish, like going to bed with a soft toy, or thinking that Santa was real.

In my second year, I met Peggy. She'd grown up in a religious home but she'd also read books on feminism and the male gaze. She would argue with men about the oppression of female bodies and watch them crumble beneath her carefully constructed arguments. She was beautiful but most importantly of all, American. It was like she'd been fed self-belief out of a can from birth. She had expensively dyed blonde hair and curves that she squeezed into tight black jeans, the top half of her spilling out of thin-strapped vests and black lacy bras. She had a rounded mouth always painted red. Men were always falling in love with her.

She was also unapologetic about her feelings on God. Most of the writers we studied had religious experiences that inspired their writing, she said. It was reductive to just erase that reality from our lectures. Once, a kid in our class argued that the word 'soul' should be banned from poetry, and she laughed in his face.

'Have you looked at our reading list?' she said, 'T.S. Eliot, Flannery O'Connor, Rilke. You think you're so post-modern erasing God from literature. Go read an actual book.' She rolled her eyes as the boy sank into his chair, a pink blush spreading up his neck.

She said atheists were just as arrogant as religious people and agnostics were the only ones she wanted to debate with. She spent six months sweeping floors and baking bread in a liberal Christian retreat before university where she went to recover from the depression that had clung to her ankles most of her life. She showed me the boxes of pills she took to keep the creeping sadness away. I didn't ask if they were working.

At twenty-two, we had both never had sex before and were uncertain how to feel about it. It was a choice we had consciously made and one we discussed in her bed late at night as we drank coffee and played Leonard Cohen on her iPod. We thought about sex all the time but were terrified of the finality of losing our virginity, a phrase we hated but couldn't find other words for.

'Deflowered.'

'Popped your cherry.'

'Given up the ghost?' I said as Peggy flung her head off the bed laughing. We hated the idea we had something men wanted to 'take' from us. We wanted to be the ones to take things away from men.

'I always thought Dean would be my first,' she said, bringing her head back up, her face mottled and pink from where the blood had rushed to her head.

Dean was her ex-fiancé and a boy she met at the Christian retreat, a quiet, serious man who worked in a bookshop. He wore heavy glasses that looked inked onto his face. Next to him in photographs, Peggy looked like she could be in an advert for freshly squeezed orange juice. They broke up a few months before she started University. A friend said he was controlling, that he couldn't cope with how men looked at her in bible studies, the way her body was like a flashing light.

'I feel like I've let my Mother down, every time a man touches me,' she said.

She sighed and did yoga stretches on the bed. Nothing we said sounded weird to each other and the comfort of it was like talking to ourselves in a mirror. Her legs were thrown over mine on the duvet. She had large moles scattered up the backs of her arms and smaller ones dotted around her thighs. Our mothers had raised us to know we were precious and our bodies too, the word 'precious' sitting lodged in our brains. By extension, this meant don't sleep with a man who doesn't also want to love you and build a life with you, and yes, marry you. We didn't trust men and yet thought about them constantly, desperate for them to notice us. Our feelings about sex and God were so closely linked, they were indistinguishable. Peggy sat up to roll a cigarette.

'God is the only thing that stopped me from killing myself that summer,' she said.

A strand of hair fell into her mouth as she spoke. She licked the cigarette paper and finished rolling it. On her bookshelf, Virginia Woolf and love poems by Rilke nestled beside books by Catholic priests who smoked weed and female bishops who were openly gay. I wanted to reach over and pull the hair from her mouth.

A few months later, when we gave in to curiosity and skin hunger and went through a phase of meeting men in bars and going home with them, we would turn up at each other's houses the next day and climb into bed to discuss it, cups of camomile tea in our hands to ease our fragile guts. We were thrilled with the fact we had touched male bodies, run our hands through the hair on their chests, and felt that strange power when we watched them crumble as we peeled our clothes off. It also felt disappointing, like we'd given in to what everyone else was doing. It wasn't what we had been promised and we thought maybe God was trying to teach us something.

'I told him I wasn't going to have sex and he said it was fine, but he didn't believe me. When I told him I'd never done it, he got all huffy and started putting pillows in the bed, like he was making a pillow fort, as if to say, 'I can't help myself.' Fuck, I hate them.' The night before, we went to a bar strung with fairy lights and people wearing berets and leather jackets and drank pints of lager, sat close together, and tripped over each other's words as we laughed and felt our bare knees knocking under the table. We had been aware of men looking at us but were enough for each other, to an extent. Gradually, men came to talk to us, mainly for Peggy, and we relented to their attention the way a cat allows you to stroke it if you wait long enough.

Later, Peggy and I drifted apart, like most people do after University. I bumped into her one night at a house party, both of us once again in her large, cream bed. She told me her first time had been with Dean. It was special, she said, looking like she was trying to convince herself. They didn't get back together. She still wore a small silver cross around her neck but I didn't know how to talk to her about God anymore. We were both lonely in a big city and we said goodbye with stretched smiles that didn't reach our eyes.

Sometimes, I told people I was an atheist. I met Joe online one summer and he told me he was reading a book about the history of humanism and he was so beautiful, so I told him I didn't believe in God. He kissed me in the corner of the pub, his mouth hot and salty. We'd been eating Nepalese food out of these rice bowls and I'd spent the entire time unsure whether I was supposed to eat the bowl or leave it untouched. He slipped his hand round the back of my neck and told me I was pretty. I kissed him back furiously.

Later, when we started sleeping together, I told him I felt a weird, empty feeling after we'd had sex. He looked up from his computer where he was watching YouTube videos about Donald Trump and frowned.

'What?'

I told him that I liked sleeping with him, it was nice, but I felt lonely afterward, even with his arm pressed against mine, the sweat sticking. He turned his computer off.

'Did I do something wrong?'

'No. You didn't. It's me,' I said, regretting mentioning it.

He rubbed his face with his hands. At thirty-two he'd already been married and divorced, to a girl he met in New York. They married for his Green Card. She cheated on him and he trailed back to London, back to living in his parents' box room. He wasn't good with opening up to people, he told me on our sixth date as we lay in bed together, his legs thrown over mine, the August heat leaving the bedsheets damp. He had deep scars up one of his shoulders where he'd dragged a penknife as a teenager and I traced my little finger into the lines there, asking if it hurt. He had slightly greying hair at the edges of his ears, got nervous when he spoke in front of strangers, and carried his height around like he was unsure of whether to stand up straight. He had shelves full of jazz records and books on social injustice in America and talked openly about how he wanted to have a kid one day. But he thought humans would turn into worm food when they died. He thought religion was for idiots, and God was a scowl in the sky. I couldn't tell him I felt less lonely when God was around. It was like trying to grip water as it spilled through my fingers, explaining it to him.

'I just get this sad feeling sometimes, like we don't connect on a spiritual level.'

'You don't believe in God.'

'Well, I do actually, I was just having a break for a while.'

He looked like he was trying to catch up with me.

'It's hard to explain,' I said, instantly feeling frustrated and sad. We shelved it.

A few months before we broke up, Joe met me in a greasy spoon cafe in East London near his house. He was going to take me on a walking tour of some cemeteries nearby, where the trees had grown over the graves and created hanging trails of ivy that made the light filter green onto the stones. He knew I liked reading the headstones of strangers. I was one of the few people he knew who wasn't afraid of graveyards. I sipped my coffee as he pulled a slightly dog-eared book out of his bag. It had a waxy red cover and there was an apple on the front with a snake winding around it.

'For me?'

He nodded. I felt my face flush. A boy had never given me a book before. He watched as I picked it up and flicked through the pages.

'It's essays about her writing and her faith. I thought you might like it.'

I opened it and started reading. It was by Flannery O'Connor, someone who had wrestled her whole life with her own conflicted feelings about God. I tucked it into my bag. My body felt like someone had run a hot wire through it. I wanted to reach over and cup his face in my hands and kiss him.

'Thanks.'

Joe shrugged and started talking about the walk we would take later. He was looking forward to showing me the graves of some local famous people. Later, as we left the cafe, I reached over to hold his hand, knowing then that it wouldn't last.

Years later, I would go on a few dates with a man from Donegal. The topic of God came up; he didn't go to church anymore, he knew who John O'Donoghue was, he still sometimes prayed when he felt anxious about something, like maybe a presentation at work. I told him about Joe and he just nodded as we sipped our pints.

'Catholic guilt,' he said.

'But I'm not Catholic, or guilty.'

He shrugged.

'Doesn't matter. The God stuff. Can't escape who you are. It's just in your bones.'

# LUCK
# Mary O'Donnell

Punctually at seven p.m. he opens a canvas bag and spreads out his professional equipment. This consists of ten common cockle shells, one speckled Deer Cowrie, and in the centre of the display, his Queen Conch, which never fails to draw comment.

He sits at the corner of a side-street not far from the Hotel Balcón de Europa and the Kronox Café. This serves the dual purpose of being visible to Nerja's surging evening crowds along the Plaza near the hotel, as well as to the passers-by drifting up towards the Town Hall.

The first fifteen minutes or so can be quiet, which allows him to observe the thriving enterprise along the street: Gabonese women plaiting children's hair, a couple rehearsing their Tango moves before they dance, later, in front of the Balcón de Europa, and a guitarist tuning up outside the wine-bar. Most of all, he watches the pickpockets, whom he identifies with by their innocent faces, as they wander up and down the street, across to the Plaza and back again, attaching themselves casually behind this or that tourist.

He'd never intended to learn the tarot. In Dublin in the mid-2000s, he had ingratiated himself into the local cultural scene mainly by helping out on the door at poetry readings and book launches and getting to know the better writers and a few well-connected academics. This approach helped him—being present, obliging, and paying attention to the more approachable writers. Gradually, elements of the city's diplomatic circles warmed to him too. He was a welcome addition to several merry dinner-parties, including one in the new US Ambassador's residence in the Phoenix Park, where he held his own and did not drink too much. He was well-read, erudite and the Ambassador was well-disposed to his soft West of Ireland accent. In the end though, he'd had to leave in a hurry and felt himself no longer welcome.

His face is darkly tanned, although a scar on his forehead, acquired two years ago when he resisted a thief in the backstreets of Torremolinos, is an irate crimson. He was lucky not to lose the left eye. His green eyes gleam beneath well-defined brows.

He concentrates again on the crowds around him. A woman approaches hesitantly. 'How can I help you, Madam?' He looks into her eyes.

She clutches a worn blue shoulder-bag, the gilt on its clasp long worn away.

'You look fatigued. Have you travelled far?' All part of a method. Solicitousness goes a long way with some of the women.

'Yes. I arrived two days ago. I'd like a reading.' English, he deduces. From London more than likely. Over the years working the coast from Marbella to Tarifa, he has acquired a working knowledge of accents from Hampshire to Aberdeen. He recognises all Irish accents automatically, and throws out a few stock Gaelic phrases which those tourists always enjoy. *Fáilte romhat!* and *Go raibh maith agat!*

Immediately, he grasps the woman's problem. He knows by her long, nervous neck and flat chest, her skinny, clueless fingers which have never touched a man, and the anxiety in her pale eyes, that she is probably a Gold Star Virgin suffering from the global disease, loneliness. The women who hunch before him rarely discuss careers, only matters of the heart. Immediately she selects several Minor Arcana from among the cards, including the Ace of Cups. Her choices are well supported by the Ace of Pentacles, indicating that her finances are in good condition. He knows not to dwell on Pentacles, and instead concentrates on the Ace of Cups, her emotional state.

'All will be well,' he murmurs quietly, not wishing the growing queue to overhear what is, after all, a confidential sitting. 'This card,' he points to a card on which are three golden Cups, 'shows that you have great emotional richness ahead.' A hopeful expression breaks across the woman's face. 'I'd even go so far to say that this person who has disappointed you, will get his just desserts.' She looks gratified. He stares into her eyes, which soften. He can tell that nobody listens to her, and as the night is only beginning and the exhaustion of listening has not yet struck, he pities her. Nobody ever looks into her eyes for more than the most functional reasons.

'You, Madam, are on the brink of something special, as demonstrated by this card—' He flicks up one of the Major Arcana, The Lovers. 'It means new beginnings!' He pauses to let the words sink in. Near him in the Café Kronos a brazier has just been lit, and the glow has created an aura around his hair. The woman's eyes rest on him, her lips slightly parted. 'Trust yourself. And I implore you to forget all the negative energy which the last man brought into your life.'

It's so basic. The woman thinks little of herself. And will continue to, regardless. Now she sits back, pleased. Convinced too, he thinks. Well, if he can make someone happier, perhaps his utterances do come true in the end. When it comes down to it, so much is suggestion.

The woman goes away, a smile on her face, having paid him 25 Euro. He pockets the cash in the large inner pocket of his apricot-coloured coat.

An hour and a half pass without incident. The Plaza is busy. The Tango dancers draw admiring crowds, inspiring some of the carefree holiday-makers to try Tango for themselves. Another woman sits down before him. Something about her causes his eyes to narrow instinctively, even as he welcomes her. Middle-aged like himself, she is tall and tanned, with springy grey hair. She wears a yellow sundress, and a heavy coral necklace nestles in the crease of breasts. He has to force his eyes away from a consideration of such breasts, gazing instead at the teenage daughter who stands beside her in high-cut denim shorts. It's a humid evening, and he begins to feel even warmer. He dares not remove the coat despite the heat, for fear of the pick-pockets who keep an eye on him.

He hunches his shoulders and spreads the cards. His eyes never leave her face as he studies her. She chooses a card. The Empress.
'A very auspicious card, Madam,' he begins, adopting his Middle Eastern voice with its rolling rs.
'Oh for heaven's sake, tell me something new!' the woman snaps, then sighs in a bored way. Hers is a well-spoken British accent.
'Sorry?'
'Tell me something worthwhile. If you can,' she challenges. From across the small table, he can smell wine and garlic on her breath.
'Madam, I normally charge 25 Euro for a reading, but in your case, and to ease your doubts, a mere 15 Euro—' The woman rummages in her bag and withdraws a purse.
'Here,' she tosses notes on the table, 'Tell me something you can't possibly know and I'll double it,' she grumbles.

A man carrying a small, tranquillized monkey passes by. 'Madam, in your case I also need to see your left hand.'
She thrusts it in his face and he pretends to scrutinize it. She has a very long life-line, he notes.
'Please select any cards.'
She turns them over with another impatient sigh.
He stares at the cards. Justice. The Devil. The Ace of Swords. He swallows again.

'Madam, you have an injustice in your life.'

'So? Doesn't everybody?'

'You were deceived many years ago.'

'Weren't we all? Excuse my language, but don't talk bollox.'

He ignores this and takes a deep breath in to steady his nerves. 'Madam, in your case a promise was made but not kept.'

At this, she seems to relent. He glances at the daughter, who observes the proceedings in between playing a game on her phone, her expression a little amused.

'The man was a scoundrel by any standards. He took advantage of your kindness.'

'That's not unusual. He was a shithead, excuse my language again. Tell me something else.'

He studies her, the fine lines, grey eyes, the straight hairline with a strong plume of darker hair to one side.

'These cards, the Ace of Wands and the Ace of Pentacles, tell me you may be a— an outdoorsy sort of woman? Gardener perhaps?'

'*Outdoorsy?* Close enough. But then you've seen my hands.' Her left hand is rough and firm, the fingernails straight-clipped and unpolished.

'Regardless, you work in the outdoors.'

'I'm starting to be impressed. I'm a garden designer.'

She tosses her head in the daughter's direction. 'You know I'm only doing this because she asked me to. All you people are charlatans. You don't fool me, even if you've picked up a few tricks along the way.'

'Madam, we don't have to continue,' he says more coolly, reaching inside his jacket pocket. He'd be relieved to return her cash.

'No. Please continue.'

He turns over another card. The Magician. 'You are a much-loved lady, great hurt was caused by your—' he hesitates, 'I don't wish to be indiscrete, but... a significant relationship within your marriage?'

The woman sits very still, her face giving nothing away.

'You confessed? To your husband perhaps?'

He drip-feeds the information. *Gently does it.*

'My daughter knows all.'

'*Everything?*'

'Everything.'

The daughter smirks. His own colour rises. A solid queue of women now snakes patiently around the corner.

'You were deceived by this person. He made promises. The person in question is no longer in your life?'

'He did, and he isn't,' the woman snorts.

Finally, softly spoken, the words that clinch it. 'But you loved him?'

He points to the Knight. The woman considers this card for a moment.

'*He* was no knight in shining armour.'

'He broke your heart?'

At this question, she softens. He tilts his head back, his face now in the shade.

'That's what it felt like! Later, all I remembered was lies and deception.' She glances at the daughter.

At this, he too looks towards the daughter. Her brown, curling hair, the lustre of her eyes beneath heavy layers of mascara and overdrawn eyebrows. The heat is almost overwhelming, the air so thick with it, he can scarcely breathe. He'll have to get rid of this woman and take a break.

'What is it you wish to know?' he asks more briskly.

'I want to know what happened him! Because I want to confront the bastard! My therapist says I should.'

'Let me assure you Madam that there is no point. You are free, because according to this card, the Hanged Man, he is no longer with us.'

'As in, D-E-A-D?' she gapes.

'Possibly. If I'm not mistaken, the man fled to somewhere southern... no, *northern*... Scandinavia, perhaps?'

'Yes! He went to Sweden. Go on,' she urges.

He turns over four cards randomly, studies them through half-closed eyes. 'This configuration doesn't augur well. He may be seriously unwell.'

'*Really* sick? *Good*, he deserves that.'

'If anything, he may be dead'. He turns one of the cards towards her. 'See this? The Page can represent someone who is a fool, even mentally unstable. He may have come to a bad end.'

The woman sits back now and grins up at her daughter. 'It's all right, sweetheart. I can relax now for the rest of my life.' For the first time the girl speaks. 'Told you so, Mummy! If you don't look, you won't find!' And she winks at her mother.

'I did hate him for what he did,' she confides again, 'but I've outlived the fucker!' She opens her purse and tosses more notes on the table without counting them. 'Thank you,' she murmurs, 'you've lifted a great annoyance off my shoulders.'

They walk away into the evening, the woman's arm resting along her daughter's waist. Relieved to be rid of them but still nervous, he decides to put up his **CLOSED TILL TOMORROW** sign, picks up the shells and cards, then drops them into his bag.

At ten o'clock he reaches his apartment. It's in an unfashionable area, but also near the hospital, a free gym and a supermarket. It suits him very well. Rebeka is waiting. She sweeps across the room and hugs him. A steaming pan of *Doro-Wat* is on the stove. He holds her in his arms, then strokes her pregnant belly. He is exhausted, and although he has stopped sweating, feels unclean.

'I should shower first,' he tells her politely.

'You never shower before you eat,' she whispers.

'Tonight is different. It's very humid out there.' More than that, he wants to wash something away. If he can wash his body down, that will do.

Fifteen minutes later, he throws himself down on the frayed sofa Rebeka has covered with a tangerine-coloured woven rug, then rubs his still-damp face thoughtfully with both hands.

'I've had a very lucky night, apart from the money.' He reaches within his coat and places three hundred Euro on the table. She gasps.

'One woman gave a third of this,' he tells her.

'Was she mad?'

'Just desperate,' he replies, 'Now buy yourself something brand new tomorrow. Nothing second-hand. A dress? The one you saw last week in that shop.'

But Rebeka is curious, and ignores this. 'Why did she pay so much?'

'The thing is… I told her something she really needed to hear.'

He decides to risk telling her more, about a time when she, Rebeka, would have been a ten-year-old in Addis Ababa with no sense of where life would bring her, and whose arms would eventually enfold her. He tells of his time in Dublin's Georgian squares, where homes were large and hosts welcoming. Of his time with the English diplomat's wife, exploring her garden and then writing about it in a newspaper column. Briefly, she became famous around the country.

Back then, his hair was cropped very short, he was beardless and unscarred.

'Everyone thought I was so clever,' he says in a low voice, 'and to tell the truth, I almost believed it myself.'

Rebeka's hands fly to her mouth, and she giggles. 'She didn't *recognise* you?'

'No.'

'And the daughter?'

'The daughter wasn't born when I left. But her husband found out. I had to leave.'

She regards him with a steady look that reminds him that she is no fool. 'Men,' she says without smiling. 'Always running away, always leaving a mess behind them. Like my father did.'

'I know I've made mistakes,' he begins, but she places her hand over his, leads him to the table.

'You have,' she replies, moving to the stove and taking the lid off the saucepan. 'But all that is behind you. I pray to Allah for you every day, because you are a good man. And even the tarot told you something tonight.'

He sits down and beholds the meal Rebeka has prepared, which she ladles into a jade-green bowl. He removes his spectacles and places them on a side plate.

# Norwegian Formula
## Kathrin Schmidt

Translated by Sue Vickerman

Norwegian Formula *first published in German as* Norwegische Formel *in Schmidt's story collection* Finito. *Schwamm drüber. Erzählungen, Kiepenheuer & Witsch, Cologne, 2011.*

My lips are cracking. I need to find a chemist and get some ointment. Or better, a chapstick. *Norwegian Formula* by Neutrogena – that's always worked well. Screaming makes your lips crack. I'm living proof. I was screaming at my child earlier on when it wouldn't leave me alone. I'd carted it off to the playground so I could quietly sort out and file the articles. I'd got myself a folder specially, and had packed the hole-punch into my rucksack along with the newspapers, put the child into the bike basket and taken myself off to this distant playground so that I wouldn't (yet again) instantly bump into a thousand acquaintances. But somehow I got it wrong. It was same as always: my child instantly attracted the other kids away from their own mothers and over to us so that within minutes, they were noisily jostling and jumping around my feet. Unobtrusively I tried shooing them away, but they were quite simply not shoo-able. Meanwhile the mothers were sitting in peace on their benches reading, knitting or just chilling out, eyes closed, their faces turned up to the August sun. Whereas my own face felt like it was icing over. I was frightened by this chill, out of nowhere. I pulled the cigarette packet from my trouser pocket. *Nails in your coffin*, Joss had called its contents. At this I felt an impulse to smile. I fumbled for the lighter; lit myself one. But the smile never made it to my face. Even closing my mouth round the filter was hard, so frozen were my cheek muscles. Give it a moment. Breathe deeply. Collect your thoughts. The first one I collected was, if this child didn't leave me in peace I'd end up killing it. Obviously this thought terrified me and I wanted to cancel it immediately. So I called my child over and started hugging and kissing it, but it was distressed by this and struggled to get away. I was still tightly hugging it when the first yell came out. *Bastard! What IS it with you, you little git? Let me get on with my own stuff JUST ONCE you cunt, you little fucker, you stupid, stupid piece of shit… bleeding little arsehole…* I raged on. Shocked, the other mothers immediately jumped up and indignantly hustled their children away. One came towards me, opening her mouth to speak, but my look was enough to make her close it again and dismiss me with a wave of her hand.

Me and the child were now by ourselves. The other mums had banded together and formed themselves into a silent cordon, fencing in their children, wordlessly taking up defensive positions at a safe distance, and digging in the sand with little spades to have something to do. My child had begun sobbing, seated desolately beside one of the two posts between which the swings were suspended. It wouldn't be hard to bash its head in with the swing's heavy metal seat. I could say its skull had got smashed by accident, but then I'd be obliged to wail and cry. I wouldn't be capable of that. So I had to let that idea go. I had wailed and cried so much in recent weeks that there was simply none of that left for the child. On the seventeenth of July Joss had been putting on his shoes. All I said was, *Why shoes, on a day like this? It's gorgeous out there; it's summer – your sandals would be more appropriate!* But he'd pulled firmly on the laces, tied them in bows, packed his breakfast into his bag and set off to work on his bicycle. The car hit him at about seven a.m. if the papers are to be believed. He didn't die immediately; an emergency doctor revived him and got him taken to casualty for treatment, but at around eleven forty a.m. his heart finally stopped. That's what the death certificate says. They gave me it the day after, but I certainly didn't give it a proper look. My mother took me in. The main thing she fussed about was making me drink enough.

My mother must also have taken over looking after the child. I ignored it. I neither got it up from its little bed in the morning nor put it back there in the evening. All I was aware of was Joss: how he'd tied his shoelaces… and hearing myself saying *Why shoes, on a day like this? It's gorgeous out there; it's summer – your sandals would be more appropriate!* I just couldn't get my head round the fact that something as inane as that was the last thing I said to him – he'd been my husband, damn it! Whenever I'd been at the bank or the council offices asking for a form for *my husband* I'd always be grinning, hardly able to utter it, because it didn't come naturally to say *I am your wife,* or *you are my husband.* Because I didn't belong to you. And you didn't belong to me. Hence I couldn't help but grin when those words loomed like an elephant in the room (– once I'd controlled the grin, the elephant would thankfully dissolve and be gone).

I haven't grinned for a long time, but have smoked too many nails in my coffin. When I pick up the child or hang out the washing, my lungs groan. As for cycling – they groan so much I sometimes have to stop and take a break.

To be honest, they're groaning at this very minute.

My child has fallen asleep, thank goodness.

When I cycle I pedal as fast as I can, which, even if you haven't smoked too many coffin-nails, can strain your lungs to bursting point. Joss was big on cycling. On Sundays we'd always go on long cycle-rides with the child on one or other of our bikes. We had a basket each: lovely old-style ones attached to the front of the handlebars so we could more easily take turns transporting the child. On that day – the seventeenth of July – Joss had actually wanted to take the child to nursery. But it slept longer than usual, so I said I'd take it later; there was enough time before my lecture. I've bought all the newspapers that reported the accident. I had for a long time hoped I might magically read that *both my husband and the child* were fatally injured. Then I'd have known better what to do. But that report was nowhere to be found. Instead, the child gradually reappeared, peering out from behind my mother's skirt, for instance, asking for a drink. My mother would then always push it a bit further in front of her and towards me, until finally it stood very close, gazing up with that look of curiosity that Joss had so adored. I hated the child for that. I never used to hate it. I would always carry it around, playing with it; talking to it. But why did it have to sleep for so long on that particular morning? If it were dead, like Joss, I'd have been able to just die. But like this, it has held me fast, not letting me go to him, *my husband.* I have to keep it clean and rub cream in and give it food and take it to the playground – where I still can't be free of it of course; not even for ten minutes in which to do my filing in peace. I can't leave the filing to the evening, because now that my mother has gone back to sleeping at her own house, I'll be in bed with the baby when it is asleep. Holding it tight in my arms. I have to attend to it, see; not just abandon it. Looking at it now, asleep in the bike basket, I have to check its head is supported, not flopping about like a big heavy flower on a too-flimsy stalk. I spend a moment carefully shifting the child into a curled-up shape so its little head is safely positioned, chin-on-chest. So that its skull won't accidentally get wrenched off. Joss would've done the exact same. Joss would probably have pushed the bike around for a while to get the child to sleep. Well, I'll push the bike around too. There's a chemist across the way, I'll go buy myself a Neutrogena chapstick. *Norwegian Formula.* I'll be careful not to wake the child up when I take it out of the basket. I mean, it really oughtn't to be left by itself on my bike. After all, someone could easily take a fancy to a child as cute as mine.

## OLD ROTTEN COVE
Christopher DeWeese

"Smells like money,"
my father always said
when the wind shifted,
nudging the stench
all the way through town
and then past it into Puget Sound.
The odor was putrid.
The sulfur of old eggs, yes,
a purple, musty flesh
machined into vapor by unseen agents.
It was hard to believe
anyone could breathe it in
without some consequence.
The closer you lived to it
the poorer you must have been,
according to the brutal sociology
the houses of our town made plain
from the pre-fabs of Castle Hill
to the doublewides behind them,
where a gas station called Sea Breeze
sold Big Bear 40s
to anyone in possession of a dollar nineteen.
At night, we'd drink them
on a derelict beach
we called Old Rotten Cove,
a place where we'd been told
two-headed fish might be seen
illuminating the seaweed
like definitive proof
of something.
We'd sit there on the logs
as the third shift burned beside us,
the paper mill rising
well lit and gleaming
like the set of a sci-fi movie,
all steel and loud and bright

as it pulverized the minutes
into bags and their byproduct,
slow catastrophe.
When our gossip ended
and we grew bored as starfish
tossed upon the logs,
we'd hop the fence
and scatter through the yard,
where piles of wood chips
mimicked the contours
of the mountains behind them
and loader trucks came and went,
tracing their rote choreographies
as tides did, the men inside each one
as automated as men back then could be
before most were replaced
by more advanced technology.
When they were gone,
we'd summit the unsteady mounds
to see how far we could jump.
It didn't occur to us then
that we were to be the evidence
of where we'd been,
our bodies like the bluffs
where the town kept ending,
which either eroded or somehow didn't
according to an obscene physiology
of luck, money, and wind.
We closed our eyes and jumped,
unsure as the moon
for those few, delicious moments
of how far it was
between where we flew
and where we might be bound.

**I was born**
Peggy McCarthy

near buckets – aluminium and red plastic,
brimming with well-water and hot cows' milk,

near drooping fuchsia and bristling heather
grazing my legs when I scouted the hills,

near old photos in the parlour press, faded faces,
their clear American smiles spanning the ocean between us.

And later by factory gates when the hooter blew
and chimneys spewed the smoky breath of a winter day,

between vinyl threads, the chords sparking,
singing through me their every turning note.

I was born when I mouthed an answer
before the question was formed.

THE RED BODIES
Lucy Holme

I

They objected to the dirty-looking stuff.
But whether bleaching left it fit for purpose, there was no actual way to tell.
They attributed its improved appearance to being bleached and moulded in that way.
Might it have worked as well without refinement? That, he could not say.
He begged to be excused from replying to any questions
relating to the chemistry of the subject, with which he was not familiar.
He only smiled and admitted his admiration for a very pretty sample of glass.
Free from bloodstains, pristine. Very pretty. Very clean.

II

A filmy not-egg rotates within the abdominal cavity.
Buoyant organ, delicate ellipse shivering, suspended whole
in sturgeon, salmon, carp, perch and cod.
Three membranous layers, too easy to infiltrate—
a simple slice and it springs open.
They praise the thickness of the lining,
consider it lore when he says
*the fecundity of the female sturgeon is remarkable even amongst fishes,*

pluck the gaseous jewels from their velvet cases
collagen sheared, manipulated by hand.
The thickening tissues oaked, softened, swelled, placed in a hemp bag
special quality credited to power and composition.
The strange romantic names they are given;
Beluga leaf, Siberian purse, short staple patriarch.
A smaller, weaker bundle of fibre is less workable, less valuable.
Ethereal levity exchanged for a liquid to clarify.

III

I see you now as you see through me.
Stretched isinglass, crafted by experts
your spidery parchment far superior to gummy gelatine.
Elegant, like the famed Russian species
with its light rose coloured ashes.
Membrane rich, bonded tight.
Spotless and free of bloodstains.
Bleached to a famously pleasing tint.

With precious sound tucked out of sight,
I stay upright most of the time.
Use hidden fins to preserve muscular strength,
keep energy conserved for swimming away.

You are an expert in your field,
in the cutting and spraying, the trickle and the seep
but still I meticulously prepare;
to prevent myself from sinking.

These curious bloodied, fleshy bodies
rendered obsolete, diminished through evolution,
through chance, through distance.

They make me more determined not to filter truth
instead become a true lung—
breathe alone and like that prized organ
once connected by an air duct rung
remain weightless, shed the heavy negative buoyancy.

*With reference to a transcript of a lecture entitled 'The Natural History of Isinglass' given by pre-eminent zoology Professor T. W Bridge at the Grand Hotel Birmingham, Thursday, February 18th, 1905 and printed in the Wiley Online Library.*

## LOOSED FROM THE GROUND AND LONGING
Sandy Longley

> *All the drama of the world is happening underground.*
> —Richard Powers, *The Overstory*

Perched on a low, oak branch
in an old-growth forest, we hear

a winter wren tremble in his
song—thirty-six, bell-like notes

every second, establishing his
territory in the understory, a little

Byron, enticing a mate to this bower
of beetles, fallen logs, brushy tangles—

song so strong and sweet it's what
we might imagine some souls

seek—boneandash, featheredandun,
when released from round spirit

holes in clay funeral urns—portals
into possibilities, a second chance

to surrender to April air. And maybe
instead of floundering, like you and

me, get love right this time around
as if their lives depended on it.

**Redux in the Blockhouse**
Michael Dooley

It was in the timber shed, as a boy, that you found the antlers.
Poking from under a pile of blocks, a stench of coniophora rot,
strange ripple that said not cattle bone, but pleistocenic Deer.
You heaved them free and slipped, sent the kettle-nest of a robin
tumbling, its ochre egg loosened into the nooks of the stack,
dropping and clacking like a pinball, a ring in a drain, a potted white.
And at night you dreamt the car-length of your head trapped
you in woodlands where you'd fled, hard-footing bracken and last willow,
twigs that made their tinder crackle long after you had passed.
You could hear the stream in which you wanted to wash the ruttish stench,
to hide you as you passed in juniper, sorrel, by the musk of a badger's set.
But the leaves have thinned for you to better see your coming end:
bay and twisted step of dog, the sun touching blades of running men.
You blare when the first teeth pierce the soft below your barrow,
see yourself cut and portioned; your crown pulled by oxen to fallow ground;
a robin dressing your sockets with lichen-moss and tufted grass.
And when you rose in the morning, picking clover from your teeth,
you saw in the bathroom mirror the nest eggs clear as Jupiters
—trembling, gassing, cracking from your eye.

# SAFE PASSAGE
## Alice Jolly

Life like steppingstones – she leaps neatly from one to the next. A gust of exhilaration filling her lungs as she hops through a mist of rainbow light. But what if she slips? She had not wanted to come to this solitary place, had not wanted to be on her own with Albie. She'd imagined the car stuck in mud, its wheels frantically spinning.

Nora, love. You'll be fine now. Enjoy yourselves. Albie needs a bit of fun.

Nora had imagined a farmer waving a devil-like pitchfork or Albie with a raging temperature. Usually they went on holiday to static caravans in Normandy with her sister's family. Albie became less painfully special when sheltered under the umbrella of those noisy, capable lives. But this year her sister was taking her family to Thailand.

No problem. We'll pay.

She couldn't accept. Old family friends had rung then and offered the cottage for free. Impossible to rent with the damp in the gable end wall. When train travel had been dismissed as too complicated, escape from their insistent kindness looked possible. A foot safely on the next stone. Until Seamus in the downstairs flat had intervened with his no-problem-at-all car.

Just the starter motor but it'll get you there.

For five years she had been deafened by this orchestra of hysterical good cheer. Yet she remained grateful for these carefully constructed conspiracies – do not let her slip – and allowed herself to be bundled into the Honda with its stained faux sheepskin seat covers and antiquated sat nav.

You need a break, love. Think of Albie. You'll do fine.

She shouldn't have worried. The journey was easier than expected and she felt stable, settled, on the side of this Herefordshire hill. The walls of the cottage leaned into the land, the radio mast at the top of the lane anchored the gusts of cloud above. The echoing bedrooms felt clammy but still Nora was grateful to the cottage. It expected nothing from her.

The week had slipped past gently. She had not merely managed, struggled through. Enjoyment, real pleasure, had turned up occasionally at the low doorways, uninvited but cautiously welcomed. She had not shouted at Albie or cried. The sun had soared impossibly high. Albie had played in the garden for many dreaming hours, making potions or bug houses.

In the afternoons, when the sun had cooled, they'd walked up the lane. It was a dead end, leading only to the farm and this cottage. The farmer's wife had left scones when they arrived, and waved once from the yard, but no-one else came. Every day she'd thought she might drive to somewhere with a cinema or a soft play centre. Proper coffee, faster broadband.

But she hadn't needed that. On the third day Albie had briefly whined about having nothing to do. Then he'd discovered an old bath embedded in an overgrown hedge. Soon he became lost in watching water boatmen skim the surface of the clotted, green water. He was six now and she was past the fevered struggle of those earliest years.

*

It was only now, their last day, that the rain had come. Nora had been warned of problems with the roof and had positioned a bucket on the landing. She could hear now the slow drops, the sound adding to the heat-beat fall of the rain on the windows and the background drips of the stiff brass taps in the kitchen and bathroom.

Nora lifted a plastic tub of craft materials from the car boot. Scissors, pipe cleaners, glitter glue, scraps of fabric and a pot of stick-on eyes. Her sister was not the only person who always had a fun activity ready for a rainy afternoon. She herself could be a proper mother, sighing kindly over spilt glue and adding water to dried up paint.

Albie made puppets out of lollipop sticks, cutting fabric to make clothes. Then a tea service out of modelling clay. She sat close to him in the armchair near the window, reading when he did not need her. Sometimes she thought of the journey home. The car had a tendency to cut out at junctions and a mysterious rattling noise sounded from the boot on tight corners.

Ridiculous, silly. She would be fine. But she would rather stay in the cottage, if only that were possible. She liked the private, dank, underwater greenness of this place.

A hermit, a recluse. She'd enjoyed Albie lying in bed until eight or later, exhausted by the long days outside. Now he was at the window.

Look a rainbow. A real rainbow.

It looped away across the distant heather-coloured hills. In London, they would pull up the frosted glass window in the bathroom, and a strip of colour might be visible, arching towards Battersea – but never a whole gasping arc of light.

Can we walk up the lane? Can we?

*

They found the snail at the place where the track to the cottage dropped down from the farm lane. He was on the cracked and pitted tarmac, making his way towards the opposite verge. Albie squatted so that he could put his head close. Look, look.

She bent down beside him. The snail was mottled brown, tawny, dark green. Its translucent antennae stood up in a V-shape, like miniature radio masts, reading the air. Its sticky, mollusc skirts undulated across the tarmac, its striped shell spiralling.

Where is he going? Albie asked. Where?

I don't know, darling. Probably just trying to cross the road.

I don't think he should. It isn't safe. He could get run over.

He might do, Nora agreed. But we've only seen two or three cars, haven't we?

Yes – but there is the tractor, Albie said.

There was the tractor – and it did have wheels the size of a small house. The driver had waved and Albie had gazed up at him, his tiny hands clasped together and pressed to his chest. His face was lit again now with that tractor enthusiasm and she was frightened by how raw he was, how new. His twig-like legs, round glasses, dinosaur T-shirt. His jagged teeth which might have to be corrected by braces.

The snail should stay with his friends, Albie says. Don't you think?

Albie doesn't seem to consider the possibility that the snail might want some new friends, that he might have argued with his existing friends.

Well, you could move him back onto the verge, Nora said. But you'd have to pick him up gently because his shell is extremely fragile.

Albie crouched, balanced the snail between his fingers, his face creased in squinting concentration as he moved with exaggerated care towards the verge and placed the snail down in the grass. Still he wasn't happy. Should they talk to the tractor man so that he could look out for the snail?

Nora reassured him that the snail would be fine. They walked back to the cottage and then on down through the rain-scattered fields. The air felt light now, a lemon sharpness cooled their skin. At the entrance to the wood, Nora waited while Albie collected sticks, pieces of moss and sheep's wool. They dawdled back up to the garden and

Albie started work on the bug houses. One had collapsed. Too much moss on the roof? Nora put the kettle on.

Soon Albie was at the door. Can we walk up the lane again?

Really?

Yes. I need to check on the snail.

I'm sure he's fine, darling. Snails are good at looking after themselves.

But can we go? Can we?

OK. If you want to.

They needed to do something to pass the time until supper. They might head along to the farm gate. A Labrador sometimes came to that gate and licked Albie's hand. Briefly Nora worried that perhaps a squashed snail might be on the lane, but she hadn't heard a car. Albie trailed a stick through the grass on the verge.

As they came close to the farm lane, he ran on ahead.

Do be careful.

She heard his running feet then a shriek. For a moment, her body was alight with fear, her breath was snagging in her throat. Surely not?

Then Albie was running towards her, laughing.

Mum, he's going across the road again.

Silly old snail, she said. He doesn't look after himself, does he?

I think I should put him back on the verge again, don't you? Albie said.

Well, I don't know. Maybe there's a reason he wants to get to the other side?

Mum, I don't think snails do a lot of thinking.

Maybe not. But he did seem to be a resolute character of snail. Don't you think? A determined snail. Stubborn even. Wouldn't you say?

Yes, Albie says and nods his head, considering the matter in depth. And that's exactly why I need to look after him.

Nora agreed to his plan. What did it matter, after all? Albie moved the snail again, placed him back on the verge. After that they walked to the farm gate to see the Labrador. Nora suggested that they go home by the other track which led around the back of the farm. She didn't want another snail conversation.

Are other children the same? The woodlice in matchboxes, the worms and spiders in shoe boxes filled with grass. Milk bottle lids used as drinking bowls, holes punched in cling film so that Albie's caterpillar can breathe. Do you think he's happy?

Yes, darling, of course. He's fine. You've looked after him so well. You've done a great job. How many times has she said that? Sometimes she did have to say - maybe he's just sleeping. Albie seemed to accept that, even when the woodlouse was clearly dead.

✳

Now they are back at the cottage and she has made boiled eggs and toast soldiers. As they eat, Albie asks about his father. Whenever they have eggs he asks because he knows that Fahima liked eggs. Nora used to avoid eggs but now she is calm, matter of fact. Albie is not upset, has never been upset. He was too young to know.

They go over the questions now, just as they always do. Yes. Not here, nowhere near here. A place very far from here. Afghanistan. A journalist.

Very far from here, Albie repeats, nods, taps his egg. Roads in foreign countries. Not safe. Very sad. Yes. Sad. Bad luck. Very bad luck. More butter? Yes.

The words are prayer, mantra, incantation. Nora thinks of a beak shaped mask, a nosegay of herbs nailed above the door. Pilgrimages, flagellation, confession. Too late for any of that. There is no end. It will always feel like constantly putting paper towels down to clear up spilt wine. No matter how many towels you use, the liquid still rises.

Soon Albie is playing with the lollipop figures again, making them tea in the modelling clay cups. Can we go up the lane again?

She says no but he is insistent.

We must go. Check on the snail.

Finally, she agrees that he can go. Only a few hundred yards. From the gate she watches him dash away and waits, waits. Steady, steady. She hears a whoop from up above and then he appears, waving windmill arms.

Mum, Mum. Can you believe it? He was going across again. Again. He was halfway across. Why doesn't he learn? I had to put him back on the verge.

She laughs with him, runs a bath, lifts a piece of twig out of his hair. The countryside has burnished his skin, his eyes now contain the distances of this empty landscape. She lifts him from the bath, wraps him in a towel, rubs his hair dry, kisses his nuzzling cheek.

*

As soon as he's asleep, she packs so they'll be ready in the morning. Cans and bottles go into a plastic bag so that they can be added to the London recycling. That half tin of baked beans will have to be thrown out. The last of the bread can be used to make sandwiches for the journey.

London anxiety is returning. Should she spend some time now trying to figure out the sat nav? How hard can it be to find your way to London? Surely home pulls you like a magnet and you find yourself there without even trying? She empties the bucket on the landing and lines it with a towel so that the dripping is less loud.

As she pulls on her pyjamas, the rain is battering on the skylight above her bed. Will the water come through the crack along the side? Time to go now, time to get back. Their luck cannot last. She pulls the duvet over her, slides towards sleep.

Footsteps on the landing. Albie stands at the door, gripping his blanket and Robby Rabbit. She stretches out her arm and pulls him into bed. His nudging knees press against her hip bone. Tucking his blanket and Robby in between them, she settles his head close to hers.

The snail?

Safe, darling. Fine.

How do you know?

Because I'm telling you. OK. I'm telling you.

He turns against her, knots his fragile fist into the collar of her pyjamas, drifts into sleep. The light from the landing falls in an arc across the bed, highlighting his tousled, sweaty hair, the translucent rim of his sea-shell ear. Step, balance, step. Hold onto the mist, the exhilaration, the rainbow light – but she will not sleep. She knows that now.

Fear walks on her skin like restless spiders. The world of Before is pulling her down. The creak of that staircase board as Fahima comes up the stairs. The light from the computer shining up onto his face as he types. His hands on the keyboard. Albie's hands. When the child is born. Definitely. Of course. I will stop that work.

She sits up in bed, finds a cardigan and socks. The rain batters above. She presses the heel of her hands hard against her eyes. They are on the journey home. She can't find the right road. Everything is a roundabout, a motorway junction, a hairpin bend. Traffic rushes past. Metal is cutting through limbs. The wheels of the car are smashing over endless snails.

Ridiculous. Stupid. She breathes deeply, lies down, dozes. Water is pouring through the skylight. Albie has gone. She's running after him up the lane, her pyjamas soaked and sticking to her legs, her bare feet splashing through mud, her hair taking flight. Some people cannot be saved.

She wakes to find Albie hot, struggling, peeling her clinging arms away. Spread your arms wide, shift your weight, find your balance. Step, balance, wobble, step. Resolute, determined or simply reckless? The water running wild around them. The heartbeat drip of the rain into the bucket. How could she tell him? How could she say?

# INSIDE VOICES
# Madeline Beach Carey

---

Neus eats her lunch every day at one-thirty in order to avoid the two o'clock rush. After twenty-three years, Eveline still always offers her wine—red or white. Eveline would like for her to drink wine with the traditional French cooking, but Neus enjoys her midday meal with a Coca-Cola, with lemon and two cubes of ice. Sometimes Neus asks for potato chips and olives along with the Coke, before the first course, if she's eating with someone from outside the museum—a friend, a visiting curator, a special foreign guest. She always lets the visitor know all the options available: wine, sparkling water, or a small glass of beer.

Caitlin considers ordering a beer. It's not warm, but it's getting there. And coming, as Caitlin does, from New York, it must feel almost like spring. Caitlin pauses. Looks around at the empty tables and then back up to Eveline, "Just water is fine."

Neus' brother-in-law has sent Caitlin. He is a publisher, a very well-respected one, who has just released the Spanish translation of Caitlin's latest novel. Caitlin is tall and slim with an elongated face and hair too fine to be worn so long. Neus is short, not even five feet, and round. Her hair is cut in the same practical pageboy she's had for almost thirty years.

Someone from the publishing house was supposed to accompany Caitlin to the Pau Serrat Foundation, but something came up—a sick child or a meeting or a parent's diagnostic test. Neus told her brother-in-law not to worry, that she would have lunch with Caitlin, walk her through the collection and the current exhibition.

"That would be perfect," her brother-in-law said.

He had meant it. Neus has been the general manager of the Serrat Foundation since its opening in 1975, but literature is what she really loves, much more so than modern art or cultural administration. She reads more than most of the people who work at her brother-in-law's publishing house.

"The thing is," her brother-in-law continued. "She isn't easy to make conversation with. A bit aloof."

"I'm sure I've seen worse," said Neus.

And she has: art collectors and the wives and children of art collectors.

Rather than difficult, Caitlin seems perfectly average, a bit insecure. She keeps name-dropping French intellectuals and providing too many details about trips to Latin American countries in support of Marxist regimes, as if her Americanness and plain face are not quite enough to elicit empathy.

Neus hasn't read Caitlin's book yet, but she certainly plans to. It has just been published in both Spanish and Catalan. A complex, sprawling novel about Spanish Republican exiles in Mexico, the Red Brigades, and the early days of the provisional IRA, it has been well reviewed in *El País*. Still, since Neus has only read that one review, she sticks to idle chit-chat. She asks what Caitlin has done so far on her book tour, where she has been, what she has seen.

"I've just been so tired," says Caitlin.

In France, last week, she was all over apparently, on the radio and interviewed twice on TV.

"They like you in France?" Neus asks, rearranging the potato chips and olives so that Eveline has room to serve the first course.

"Beet salad," says Eveline, placing a bowl down in front of Caitlin. "And the leek soup."

Caitlin picks over her salad and says, "I think they understand what the book is talking about in France."

Neus looks out the window at the sculpture garden just below. She studies the tourist families spreading out blankets, weighing down the corners with their shoes and backpacks. She forgets about Caitlin for a moment and then comes back to her: the sharp, pinched face, the thin lips painted red.

"We have trouble," Neus says, "with the tourists. They leave their bags on the ground in the sculpture garden and then, whoosh, the thieves sweep in quick as can be."

Caitlin chews politely, swallows, touches her lipstick, then launches into a story about a trip with her husband from Italy, by boat and then lorry, to Albania, of getting robbed in a tiny square—passports, belt buckles, everything. Neus isn't really listening. She's thinking that there aren't many people in the restaurant. Maybe because it is still March and all the tourists have yet to arrive.

"Or because they're all outside. It's such a sunny day," Caitlin offers.

It's the first time she has seemed kind or at all genuine.

Neus shifts on her chair. Her right hip is acting up, a familiar tightening, a little vice squeezing the joint. She notices that Caitlin is wearing a long, thin, silver necklace with a shark's tooth on it. Her bright red Converse sneakers stick out below the table. Instead of a necklace, Neus wears a lanyard with her ID card around her neck. She really should make more of an effort to wear necklaces, or any kind of jewellery. Albert gave her earrings last Christmas, tiny gold hoops with delicate hatching and a necklace that matched. Neus isn't even sure where they are now.

"Do you have children?" Neus asks, even though she once heard her brother-in-law say that Americans don't like being asked direct questions.

"No," says Caitlin. "No, we don't."

Neus is slicing her lamb. Caitlin, who originally wanted just one course but was talked into two, studies her chicken tagine, removes the ceramic lid and tries the couscous first.

"I had children late," says Neus. "I didn't meet my husband until later in life."

Caitlin's face softens a bit, "Really? How old were you?"

"Thirty-four when we met. We had both been married to other people. By then I was ready, you know? I had my daughter at thirty-six, my son two years later."

"I'm about to turn forty-one," says Caitlin.

"Oh, but nowadays there's still time."

"I don't think we want to," says Caitlin. "My husband just got tender. Sorry, I mean tenure. It was a real slog, years and years of struggle."

She doesn't seem very curious for a writer. She doesn't ask about the museum or the city or even the food, which is prepared daily by Eveline and her assistant, and has been for almost a quarter of a century. The Serrat is the only museum left in the city with a proper restaurant. Everywhere else a chain runs the cafeteria; rice timbales and paellas arrive vacuum-packed each morning, ready to be microwaved for the lunch crowd. Here, all the ingredients are fresh.

Neus thinks about how things have changed. When she married Albert, she couldn't wear white. It was somehow shameful, getting married so old and for the second time. Nowadays, you really could wait and have children at forty-one or forty-five. Nobody got married in white. They had gone to a wedding last year where the couple already had three children running around the lawn of a modern hotel in the Empordà.

"I didn't think I wanted to have children until I met Albert. Then I really wanted to have them with him."

Neus wonders of course if that *was* what she really wanted. It isn't the children who have given her so much joy; it's Albert. She would have been just fine with him, with their trips to Paris and Budapest, with their books and late-evening walks. She likes to argue with him about politics. They basically agree on the need for a Catalan Republic, but they clash over certain nuances. Neus, when she was a bit younger, really liked to fight it out over a long meal— her with her Coca-Cola, Albert with his wine, followed by two coffees with ice. She liked getting into the nitty-gritty of policy. But they don't argue like they used to— it's too easy to agree now on the idiocy of all politicians, of the failings of the Spanish state.

Albert is at home now, perhaps reading Caitlin's novel, which arrived in the mail yesterday. But more likely he's watching political talk shows on Channel 3. He retired two years ago at sixty-five, when Neus could have retired as well. But what would she have done at home all day? She already read a book a week and went to the theatre and the cinema every weekend. Without working, she would have gone mad. She could, of course, have taken care of Albert. But there is Elena, a woman who makes his lunch and then cleans and irons while he reads the paper. His heart is failing. They are waiting for a new one. Neus, at home, would just make it all worse. All her nervous energy would highlight his decline, show how slow and easily tired he's become.

"What about the independence crisis?" Caitlin asks.

She has declined dessert but Neus insists on the *illa flotante*, saying they could share.

"Well," Neus says, speaking for herself and for Albert, "we're very much affected. I mean we've gone back thirty years. People are in prison! My husband's nephew could be indicted soon. It's terrible."

"Like the Franco years," said Caitlin.

"With this right-wing party in power," said Neus. "Rajoy! We were considering leaving, moving to Portugal."

Neus doesn't explain that the move to Portugal wasn't entirely related to the political environment but rather to a job managing the new Serrat wing at the Serralves, an offer she could not accept because her husband is waiting for a heart transplant. She carries a special phone provided by CatSalut with her at all times. They will be contacted on that phone. He is high up on the list; has been for close to a year now. When a heart becomes available, they must be close by. They have been told to remain within a forty-kilometre radius of Hospital Clinic. There was never any real possibility of going to Portugal and yet the neighbouring state has taken on a mythical status in Neus' imagination. Porto now seems like everything they had hoped Barcelona to be in their youth: a cultural beacon, a northern coastal city nestled safely in the cradle of social democracy. It's been a year since they've even been to their house near the French border. It's a lot these days to even go to the cinema, Albert wheezing, Neus checking her pocket obsessively for the phone.

Caitlin stores this away: a couple, professionally dedicated to Catalan culture for the past forty years, considering exile in Portugal. The women have finished the *illa flotante*. Caitlin admits after prodding that, yes, it was really good. When the coffee arrives, Caitlin asks, "Will we be able to see the archives? I would love to see the drawings of Mont-roig."

"Of course," says Neus. "After we see the shows we can go downstairs. I have all the time in the world."

She motions to Eveline that they have finished.

The reason Neus is so willing to spend so much time with Caitlin, despite the fact that she doesn't find her at all charming or engaging or particularly knowledgeable about Catalan culture or the work of Pau Serrat, is that she prefers being in the galleries to being in the offices today. As they walk through the first few rooms, past the earliest work,

Neus watches Caitlin in her blue jeans and red shoes and bright yellow "RESIST" tote bag and says, "Let me take your picture, you match the paintings."

Caitlin isn't enthusiastic about having her picture taken but turns, pulls her shoulders back, and smiles obediently.

Financially, things are not going well at the Foundation, which relies on a small subsidy from the Barcelona City Council but for the most part survives on ticket sales. After the Catalan independence vote and the images of police beating protesters, tourism has steadily declined. Tourists—well-off French and English, cultured Americans, Russians, Japanese—don't want trouble or commotion. Many of the people who visited the city for its art and architecture go other places: Madrid, Lisbon, or more up-and-coming cities like Porto and Ljubljana.

The numbers have been looking grim for well over a year. But Neus, a few months back, just put on blinders. Ever optimistic, she dismissed the trustees' talk of catastrophe and, as always, forged ahead. No exhibitions were cancelled or postponed. No changes were made. Nothing was mentioned to the Serrat family or to most of the trustees. Neus had other ticking time bombs to deal with: Albert's pacemaker and that phone that never said moo but was always there like a lead weight in her pocket.

Three weeks ago, the board decided that drastic steps must be taken. The restaurant—slow, overpriced, full of sugary desserts and overly rich French dishes—would be closed and replaced with a self-service cafeteria. Also, six members of the office staff would be laid off. Neus has the six names and the compensation packages for each one of them in an Excel file called "Contingency." She knows each and every one of the six personally—Christ, she hired all of them. Mercè and Arnau started working at the Foundation in 1984, the year Neus met Albert. Mercè, Arnau, and Maite all came to Neus' wedding. Laia drove Neus to the hospital when Albert had his first heart attack—the only time in her life she didn't feel up to riding her moped.

Last night, while Albert slept with the TV on, Neus sat at the kitchen table trying to convince herself it was fair to fire any of these people. Mercè, for example, has been so lucky in other ways in life. She is still beautiful in her late fifties, with lovely, dewy skin and a tiny waist, and her husband is a doctor so it isn't as if they're going to starve. Maite is single and not pretty, but she knows lots of people. She is a generous person, a good friend, an excellent conversationalist. Someone might give her a job. But Neus knows that this is highly unlikely. People don't hire post-menopausal women—especially ones who get fat and carry on as if they haven't. But it's not as if Maite will live in poverty. She owns her flat outright and her family will help.

Neus herself knows nothing about financial hardship. Her father, also a voracious reader, was a notary, so the family remained financially stable, even in the darkest period right after the civil war. Their problems with the regime were ideological but well-hidden, their post-war grey but comfortable.

She doesn't know much about financial difficulties, but she does know about being humiliated, ignored, overlooked, invisible. So, Neus worries about Maite. She knows it won't be easy for her. Neus is frumpy, even frumpier than Maite. She is not pretty, but she is smart. She is also considered to be genuine and kind. A good person, feisty but always fair. But Neus knows that such reputations can change.

The new director, hired last summer, is English and very happy to be in Barcelona. He's fifty-two, with a thirty-year-old wife, a new baby, and very expensive wire-rimmed glasses. He told Neus they were doing the right thing, what had to be done.

"Let's tell them together," Neus said, just a few days ago.

She envisioned using the auditorium, one of her favourite spaces in the building, octagonal in shape, with walls covered in natural beech and an impressive mural painted by Serrat himself framing the stage.

"A bit dramatic," said the new director.

So they planned to tell everyone today, in the committee room on the second floor where they usually had Monday morning staff meetings with coffee and assorted tea cookies. But last night, while Neus was sitting at her kitchen table, the director texted to say he was off to London, to the Tate, to give a conference on the challenges of audience engagement. He had mixed up the flights and was leaving today.

Caitlin is studying the *Hope of a Condemned Man* triptych rather intently.

"So he was producing these in exile?" she asks.

Neus snaps back into focus.

"Well, he didn't leave. It was an internal exile."

Caitlin writes that down in her notebook. Neus decides she will tell everyone tomorrow. Arnau does the books, controls all the accounts. Perhaps he could get hired in the financial sector. That would mean longer hours, maybe a commute. Arnau, not exactly extroverted, is very good at his job, obsessive, meticulous. Arnau has two children and his wife is a nurse. They pay a hefty mortgage, close to 2,000 euro a month. He knows exactly how much Neus and the director make, how many of each of his monthly salaries equals just one of theirs.

One of her phones vibrates and, for a brief moment, Neus thinks it is the heart phone that has moved. But, alas, it is her plain, old, everyday work phone buzzing with a message from her brother-in-law asking how lunch went.

It's still going, thinks Neus, as she guides Caitlin into the next room.

## A DOLL ADDRESSES ITS MAKER
Patrick Deeley

So much you never expected would happen —
that you would sculpt me, for a start,
but when your fingers got busy
between swaddling your children and finding
a place to rest for the night,
you whittled limestone with a spike of antler
or shard of slate, until your hands
bled. You'd stop and start, fling me from you
in a spark of temper — retrieve me later,
ask your eldest or ask the wind
that stirred the smoky, open kindle until
it burst into flame, how much longer
must you spend tricking my braids of hair,
or dreaming the button-head pose
you knew would conceal my face, or settling
my arms to rest on my breasts,
or following the flow of my belly and thighs
down to where the absence of feet
in effigy of so powerful a walker as you were
could stand as a quiet joke. I grew
even as you clipped and littled me
the half-spit of yourself, curvy and burly,
exaggerated too. So fettled,
I found myself dipped in a blush of red ochre.
Carried everywhere, sometimes sticky
with animal grease or smudged
with berry juice, depending. Whispered to
in the dark, a bosom friend
you could hear whispering back through hurt
and hunger, the harangue of hard weather.
You'd forget me as you stretched
with the lengthening of light, airy and clean
as birdsong. I turned up at Willendorf
long after you were gone. Visitors
to the museum where I'm on display mimic how
you turned me in your hands, your story
of creation continuing, so many
sunsets yet to pass before the work is done.

SLANT
Animashaun Ameen


We were in your room, naked, smoking
bad weeds & eating peppered snails. Our limp dicks
dangling beneath us like pendulums readying
themselves to smash anything into orgasm.

> You made a comment about how dark my skin is &
> we both laughed so hard everything sparked into existence.
> Maybe it was our chemistry. Heck, maybe it was simply the weed
> turning our brains to mush and giving everything else more colour
> than they deserve. I asked you to open the windows

but instead, you opened your body to let the beast
inside of me in. Your pupils dilated with sheer hunger
as I tear into your body & made a home out of it.
I am a bull, rough. You are a rose, thorny. In another reality,
we go together like bad weeds and peppered snails.

> We both finished and we stood in front of the huge mirror
> in your room, our reflections staring back at us as we inspect
> the art we made on each other's bodies.

> *I love you, Ameen.*
> *I know.*

I have seen the world and you have seen me naked,
in a way, you have seen all that I have seen. You plucked
your hopes from the sky and asked me why I never say it back.
Here, I let out a little laugh. Here, it is not about bad weeds
or broken chemistries.

> I kissed you goodnight and left you with
> more darkness than I had intended to. On the walk back home,
> I asked myself why I never say it back.

# Two Poems
## Sarah McCartt-Jackson

### ENDNOTE

How many times will she go back
because she *loves* him, don't you see,
how she loves the way he holds her
throat inside his fist like a bird.

Because she loves him, she doesn't see
how an avocado tree drops its fruit
when it's already too ripe to eat, her
fingernails slip beneath the bruised skin,

how an avocado tree droops its fruit-
heavy head toward the sandy yard, the gravel
that slips beneath her bruised skin
when she falls, and she falls hard with a knee

heavy on her head toward the sandy grave
of an unborn daughter, whose eyes were like
Green River Falls in the beginning. And she falls hard.
She fills her empty suitcase with bottles of wine

that take the shape of her unborn daughter. Eyes
green as a bottle lip, a desert vine that's always thirsty.
She empties her suitcase, fills herself with bottles of wine,
with how many times she will go back.

SILHOUETTE

She crawled through whale bones
at the museum, smiled at me—no.
She didn't know I was there. I wait

until she goes to sleep to throw away
her paintings. Can't keep them all
magneted to the fridge door where they pile

up until, too heavy, they scatter like poplar
blooms in early June, orange tulip cups
rain-collected and lipped with tiny ants.

When I read to her, she tells me, *I see you*
*even though I'm not looking at you,* her eyes
blue like his, her voice a struck piano wire.

I have slept in many strangers' beds: once,
drunk, I listened to two philosophers
study outdated maps pinned to a wall.

Once, I slept off a heavy bloody mary
on top of the coats at a Super Bowl party until
a dog nudged me awake with its cold nose.

Once, my best friend in college took my hand
and led me away from someone
else's dorm, from someone I didn't know.

Once, on a futon, in a garage with a rattling air
conditioner unit that was partially melted
by an overturned lamp, a man I loved put his fingers

around my throat until I couldn't breathe while he
looked at me through blueglass eyes, as if he couldn't
see me. That's when I knew I didn't know him.

And then the sun rose. And I made coffee
from yesterday's grounds and tipped my cigarette
ash into his mug. One small revenge at a time.

I think of her face like trying to dig a hole in sand
by the ocean, always filling itself with the tide.

THERE IS NOTHING MORE BEAUTIFUL THAT LANGUAGE CAN OFFER
Patrick Holloway

Her breath a herald. My hand slippery
with sweat in hers as she squeezes
everything inside out. Hot scream,
still wet from her living
you are carefully handed over
with gummy emerald eyes.

✻

Little bird: chapped, red folds
of skin. Your tongue flicking inside
your newborn mouth. Endless gums
gather endless screams. I hold you
to my chest. I no longer sleep
but nap in between fleeting moments
of silence. I hide your eyes from the light
as I change you. Your twig legs kick, the dummy
falls from your mouth and you overwhelm
the world with your yowl.

✻

My phone rings incongruously
& her voice is thick, it comes
from a place I have not been yet.
She rolled off the bed, come home, quick.

✻

You shape your lips around
English & Portuguese, thudding
the fat, thick tongue against palate
to create new sound. On my lap
you soothe my nose & say
I love you too much. & I say
my girl, my girl, & you say

my daddy, my daddy & I think
there is nothing more beautiful
that language can offer.

*

A terror thunders inside of me
when twilight is at its darkest.
I see you falling down stairs, a crack
I feel in my bones as your head swirls
sanguine, clotting your thin blonde hair crimson.
That moment I turn in the supermarket
& you are lost & everyone obscures
into ghostly shapes with no eyes.
How can love do this & how can I live
forever with this inside of me?

*

It is too hot & you are falling into sleep
in my arms. Sticky from the heaviness
in the air. I see it, the exact moment you fall
into the seemingly ceaselessness of dreaming.
If I had only a moment to anchor me to this
terrain, it would be this, your weight
in my arms, the mass of you that holds
all of my love, sticky & tangled, the flesh
of what it is to live.

# FOUR POEMS
## Gerry Murphy

---

### THE POETS

In the Capital,
the poets developed a reputation
for 'stepping-on-their-own-tongues'.
They would become evasive at questions
and study their shoes (gifts from the Emperor)
while their rasping tongues
would squirm and slither beneath
like snakes.

### KISSING AND SPEAKING

Lying together briefly
in the early morning light.
You, just in from night-shift,
I, about to get up and head off to work.
Your spiky new hair-cut
the hot topic of conversation
when we are speaking,
when we are not kissing.

LUNA
(after Richard Tillinghast)

The full moon afloat
in the southern sky.
Its stony Buddha face,
worn away by time
and the boots of astronauts.


LUNA II
(in the style of Lorca)

Like a child
who has been playing
all day long in the forest,
then turns up at your door
asking for her supper:
the moon.

## PORCELAIN
Rachel Coventry

Sometimes,
if you grasp
the concept, you
don't need to see
the art. A urinal is
a urinal after all. I
imagine their faces
in the gallery, looking
at the Fountain; some are
aghast, some are clever and knowing,
some are bored because they have seen the
future. Of course, whoever's seen the future is bored.
Now, it is clear a concept is not enough because-some
faces are clever, some are bored. Despite this, if I could
decide on what concept best fits this poem, I'd save  you
the time it takes to read it. Even though everything has
changed since then. Your faces are inscrutable
and the fountain in the Tate is not
even made of porcelain.

EGYPTIAN WING
Heather Treseler

Lost, in the museum, on Saturdays in the wine-dark
rooms of Egyptian tombs because my mother
had a disorder of the blood and no one
would tell me anything I could
believe of death—

her bed raised high as an ancient altar of stone
worn by a priest's blade: there, she lay
cordoned off, beyond touch, like
a carved artifact the centuries
have filigreed with hairline

fissures of light. I was told to pray to the poor
man who hung, lashed to his lumber,
his ribs a staircase to a face of agony
strangely cleansed of terror: this
was no god to save a mother—

whereas the Egyptians had followed a creed
of birds: even the tomb was called an egg.
And while "mummy" an accident
of sound, not sense, there was
tender swaddling in the

death clothes, each body bathed in Nile salt
and stuffed with fragrant spices, organs
parsed in Canopic jars like the
grammar—subject, predicate—
of a sentence. To be sent

off, as if to summer camp, with pets, snacks,
and details for care and handling:
for that afterlife, I prayed to
falcon-headed Horus,
weigher of Ka,

soul of the heart. Weren't birds commuting
between a bitter earth and sky? Making
an eros of pitched precision?
Mothering a small body
toward its horizon.

## XENA
Susie Berg

I push my pale, freckled nose right up to Xena's,
which is black and spongy, and covered in raised bumps
like the skin of a basketball. Her breath smells meaty.

Her ears, and the patches patterning her cottonwood-white fur,
are caramel, they are golden demerara sugar, they are the baked-brown
underside of a cookie. I sniff and expect cinnamon, vanilla.
Mostly I smell fur. Fur and meat-breath. A hint of cheese.

When Xena lies on her back for a belly rub, her mouth
falls open, her cavern of bared teeth a reminder:
we two are animals. She, more than me,
thirsts for flesh, her pointed incisors piercing my skin
in her puppy way. She intends harm, that's how she's built.

She takes the cheese right from my palm, noses at the morsel,
works her lips and tongue until she has it all. Xena licks my damp hand
and I regret, for a minute, not being the kind of mother
who fed my child from my own mouth, who chewed meat
to place it between my baby's gums.

Xena yips. Her brown eyes beam into my pupils until
the muscles that wrap the cage of my chest lift like wings,
then settle. She inhales. The hill of her body shakes,
the wave of her fur a current of wind over grass.

We sit this way several times a day, woman and dog.
She is teaching me how to breathe.

## HOME INVASION
Mark Ward

Lately, everywhere smells of piss,
cat piss particularly, piss

as pungent as a mad bitch
caterwauling, carping, all piss

and vinegar over nothing:
fresh water, food, litter; still, piss

as punishment, piss like a snitch
whispering names, death warrants; pissed,

he burns down the house, dousing
it in his only liquid: piss

in corners, on clothes with your smells,
where he knows you alone walk: piss,

and it's only when I list this,
I realise he's taking the piss.

It's hard to take when family
turns on you. We sleep, wake to piss

and a shit out in the open,
having made the house cornerless.

*There has to be an end to this.*
I nod. The cat glares, starts to piss.

PUERTO LOPEZ
Mark Roper

I dreamt I was bringing a horse
in from a field.

The long, gentle weight of its face,
the shy watered eye.

The quizzical shudder of breath,
smell of leather,

smell of sweat, ancient grass, faded light,
of meadowliness.

I woke up and went for a pee.
Through a window

I found I could see, in a tangle
of undergrowth,

the round head of a pigeon, fired
by a streetlamp.

Its face was the face of the horse
which was my face.

# A Body in Solitude
## Emily Cooper

### 1.

I want to dance. I dance in a garden in Devon, watching those around me, their joints loose, no cares. I feel stiff, contained, metallic. I dance but it doesn't get inside me. Closed eyes, giddy on cider, my moves are contrived, stolen, my limbs are shorter than they are meant to be, but feel so far away.

### 2.

I swim in the sea with my friend and her mum. They dip their heads under the water, we move with the waves, letting them suck us out into the bay. I feel out of control, detached. They're bigger than me, horses to my Shetland pony. It is high tide and smooth rocks are suspended inside the white waves. I get knocked under. My friend pulls me up before I hit the loose bed, braces me with her body as we are pummelled by wave after wave. I have pebbles in my bikini; I slowly unfold myself, scratching them out onto the beach as she tells her boyfriend how I nearly died.

### 3.

I want to get in touch with my body but yoga enhances my narcissism. I convince myself during each class that I am the best, or at least the fastest improver, imagining that everyone is silently in awe of my flat-footed downward facing dog. I repulse as much as impress myself. Meditation makes me grumpy. I leave classes bad tempered. The first meditation class I went to in Bethnal Green, a man fainted and knocked his front tooth out. No one got up to help him. Someone picked up the broken tooth and handed it to him and he quietly left. I found myself saying just loudly enough for the room to hear "they won't be able to fix that". I couldn't trust meditation, or myself, after that.

## 4.

Sex is no longer an option. I have to get up if a man sits too close to me. Dinner in a half empty restaurant with a male friend makes me so claustrophobic that I have to go outside. At a wedding I strain not to let the uncle I dance with know that I can't cope with his proximity, I have to pretend to mess up the céilí moves over and over to avoid getting too close. I want to want sex, I want to want to be touched, I want to want the weight of someone in the bed beside me, the clammy skid of palms across muscles, the stretch of a spine bent back out of formation, but, I don't. I can't and my body won't let me.

## 5.

I listen to a podcast about two books that both feature women getting kicked in the vagina. This, of course, shocks me. The podcast presenter describes cowering physically on the tube as she read the passages. The author (who is French, this seems somehow relevant) goes on to explain that many women just don't enjoy sex, they feel so much less than they expect they are supposed to that they push the boundaries of pain in order to feel anything at all. I think about it all night, talk to people about it, mention repeatedly about women getting kicked in the vagina. I consider my own predicament; I have felt it all so intensely that I don't want to feel it at all. I want isolation from it, from sexuality, from intimacy, from the pain.

## 6.

Swimming in the sea helps, but I only want to do it for an audience. I find it so hard to get in if there's no one to watch or tell me how brave I am. I like to do it naked for maximum impact, but it's hard to do that on your own. I find a set of steps at the end of a pier on Inch Island and undress and swim out, shielded by the concrete. When I'm walking back along the pier, a group of boys have started fishing. Late teens, black band t-shirts. They can't catch my eye when I say the obligatory hello. They've seen me pale all over, the bruises all up my thighs, the way the tips of my hair are wet at my neck though I didn't dip my head, they know the damp shape of my breasts under my shirt. They are more ashamed than me. But I don't swim there again.

## 7.

I notice how editors cut the bloody bits of my writing. Where there are cuts and haemorrhages and clots, they put blank spaces. Too bodily, too raw, too uncomfortable. My poetry becomes more and more brutal; I pull the skins off eels and splatter the walls with blood. I cut my friend's hymen for her, holding the doctor's scissors like they are my own.

Slicing as if with fabric scissors, wide open, sliding with satisfaction. I feel the way my body pours itself out every month, empties what is already vacated.

## 8.

It's hard to live in the present tense. It's always getting caught up by the past. The future glares back at me, blinding me with grey hairs, with changed plans and lists yet to be ticked off. Things improve momentarily then get worse, the trick of progression, always sliding downhill, a magic road that fools you, not through magnets or gravity, just a stupid trick of the eye. Nothing really gets much better; it just shifts to the side.

## 9.

I go to India to be alone. This in itself is a contradiction. Delhi on its own has a population three times that of Ireland. Even so, I manage it somewhat. Before I leave, I am warned by everyone about the dangers, how I will be followed by men and not to get buses alone. I become worried about what clothes I can wear, which exposed extremities would get me into trouble. I search the Internet for information of whether jeans are ok, or if I have to cover my shoulders, if a slip dress in the heat would be acceptable. I become fixated on my body, what is decent or indecent.

## 10.

I consider that this fixation on solitude is a kind of bluff. That what I really want is for someone to see my demonstration of independence and find it attractive. I speak to an Indian/Australian artist about her work and life while we are on the Delhi Metro in the Ladies' Carriage. We have both just read *Simple Passion* by Annie Ernaux and the idea of obsessive love is our topic of the day. She describes how she had become fixated on her first boyfriend's independence. How his solitude held an importance that hers didn't. She felt her time alone was tinged by a desperation that she couldn't attach to his. She wanted it; she was obsessed more by this idea of self-possession than she was by him.

## 11.

There is a solitude in being in your body, in feeling it through your nerve endings and muscles. It is in those bracing moments of cold water swimming or dancing, eyes closed, in a crowd or alone, that you can honestly feel self contained, as if the air around you becomes more clear and pure.

## 12.

Ironically, I started to investigate and practice solitude while I was involved with a man. The relationship made me deeply unhappy, yet I was completely entranced by him. His constant acts of denigration towards me meant that I became somewhat detached from myself. I began to look back at my own body and self as if at a stranger. As I was fixated on him, I became fixated on my faults: selfishness, lack of generosity, a litany of physical problems that seemed impossible to cure. Even as I justified myself - to him, to my friends, my family — so he made apparent other aspects to which I should attend. As a result I became smaller, not just metaphorically, physically.

## 13.

I have never had much drive to be thin, I've worked hard all my life to allow myself pleasures without guilt, let my body fluctuate in order to enjoy it as it is. (A friend once told me to appreciate a man with a belly; a man who knows how to indulge his appetite in food is more likely to be indulgent in the bedroom. This is the attitude I take to my own body, if I get a bit of a belly, I consider it 'luxury fat', a mark of what a good time I have been having.) I lost two stone over a few months, unintentionally. I would wake up in the morning and vomit as I brushed my teeth. I just physically couldn't get any food inside me. I repeatedly visited the doctor. After an appointment when I broke down crying, she sent me to get an endoscopy and an ultrasound. I needed proof that what was happening to my body was real and concerning. My body was an obsession, it felt like it was failing me, it was taking his side, forcing me to become stiller, quieter, lesser. The investigations all came back clear.

## 14.

I begin to get used to being alone. I find myself wanting to push myself into doing things that make me feel uncomfortable. I drive out to a gig in a village on the north coast of Donegal; drink pints of Guinness and dance to a Guinean guitar band. After the music finishes I sit outside and a man approaches me, telling me that he noticed me dancing alone. Someone takes a photo of me. I begin to feel like a spectacle. I buy a round of brandies and soon they're telling me their deepest secrets. People love over-sharing when you're on your own, it's like they can't imagine you'll ever have company to spill their beans to. After a few more brandies I'm invited up to a hotel room but instead go out to sleep in my car on the beach. Curled up in the backseat, I wake up in the morning and consider a swim but instead open up all the windows and drive home with the music up full blast — unconvinced of my own sobriety.

## 15.

I do things that seem unwise – things that people warn me not to do. I climb mountains alone. At the top of Muckish I meet two men, each with a wooden staff. We stop and discuss how Dunnes Stores were doing a sponsored walk up here that morning. *The whole company?* I ask and we share an awkward laugh. As they walk off to see the massive erected cross on the moonlike summit, I stumble down the path thinking about how they could very easily kill me and cover me up with rocks and no one would know where I was, had I not just posted a series of instagram stories about getting to the top.

## 16.

In India I go off by myself to the Himalayas, walk the freezing streets of McLeod Ganj, thinking some kind of spiritual awakening might happen. Instead I just get very cold and drink hot ginger-honey-lemons. On the way back down to New Delhi, the bus drives through an overly large pothole and busts a wheel. They keep driving; the ominous thud thud thud of the split tire makes it clear that we'll have to stop. It's the middle of the night, we're in the middle of nowhere on a small road surrounded by paddy fields and the occasional shack. I look down the bus. I don't see another woman. Well, this is it, I think. My phone is dead from listening to podcasts. We stop at the side of the road. There is a house with dozens of tires outside it, all shapes and sizes. I watch as the driver and another man go to knock on the door. There is a light on in the garage. They knock again and walk around looking at the tires. No one answers. We drive on, thud thud thudding down the narrow road, as we speed up the thuds get faster. My death approaches. After some time we stop at a bus stop, they tell us to get off and we stand at the side of the road. I see another woman with a backpack. The relief. At least if we die, we'll die together. Another bus arrives and we get on. I sit beside a man who quickly begins to snore loudly. Somehow we get to Delhi before our expected arrival time.

## 17.

I start to really enjoy strangers touching me. My yoga instructor rubs scented oils on her hands and lifts our heads and pushes our shoulders during shavasana, I really look forward to going to her classes. One day she only pushes my shoulders and I feel very disappointed. Skin hunger is a widely recognised phenomenon. In studies of orphans during the mid 20th century when people were discouraged from showing children physical affection, some children were witnessed failing and even dying as a result of lack of touch. Experiments on baby monkeys showed that they would chose a soft mock mother that they could cuddle to a wire one that provided milk. We need to be touched.

## 18.

Pleasure from touching happens periodically throughout life, we aren't supposed to enjoy it really, the tickle of getting our feet measured as a child, the dentist who inadvertently leans across you, those accidental brushes of hands when getting change in a shop. These thrills are secret and almost shameful, but contact has its own kind of nourishment. When you're practicing physical solitude, each one takes on more importance, a small increment towards stopping the lack of touch driving you mad.

## 19.

I look at the naked pictures of myself on my phone. My head cut off. Tan lines though I hadn't been in the sun. He sent them back to me over and over when he found out I'd been with someone else. He wanted me to be ashamed and that's how he was doing it. *Look at yourself, you're disgusting. This is what you are: flesh, wrong. Be ashamed.*

## 20.

I work as an extra to make money. The days are long and boring. Usually we sit for hours, trying to keep warm. You learn very quickly where you belong on the pecking order on set. There is always a shifting hierarchy: assistant directors vie for supremacy, make up artists bitch about the cast, everyone is terrified of the director. In all of this there is an understood certainty: extras are below everyone. On set you are told to move, in specific ways, contradicting specific ways, by different people, to be acted out in the same way. You learn to do what you're told, ask as few questions as possible, smile, to disappear into the background. A cameraman very clearly told me that we were props. Human props. I take a job that pays at least twice as much as a normal job. It is a soft porn shoot, a fake soft porn shoot. It turns out that a fake soft porn shoot is the same as a real soft porn shoot. My mother laughs when I tell her, says my boobs aren't big enough. They dress me in lingerie, ask me to kneel on an unmade bed wearing handcuffs. I comply. They tell me to look over my shoulder. To spread my legs wider. To put my hand on my arse. After we finish I hold up a laminated sheet that says 'Trafficked Woman'. As I leave, the photographer tells me that he much prefers shooting the extras. He says the cast are too concerned about how they look.

## 21.

I finally read the book they were talking about in the podcast. Technically she gets kneed in the vagina, but that doesn't diminish the impact. The book unsettles me. It is about a woman who is desperate not to be alone, who destroys all of her relationship with this desire. Her constant insatiable need for physical contact, with anyone, means she is ultimately alone. The unerring forgiving love of her husband is no compensation for her drive to be touched, felt, abused. The last scenes of the book are set the night of her father's funeral. She gets obliterated and goes to a bar and dances. I remember that that's the same reaction I had after my father's funeral. The relief of processes completed, the paralysing grief swept aside for a moment as I danced alone, eyes closed, upstairs in a bar in my hometown.

# ANTHOLOGIES FROM SOUTHWORD EDITIONS

## Poems from Pandemia

Editor Patrick Cotter

In April 2020 the publishers put out a call to poets to submit works of hope or its lack, which were about Covid-19 or an historical / fantasy plague; poems which were autobiographical / confessional or surreal / allegorical. The result is a collection of brilliant work by both established and emerging poets from across the English-speaking world, from Australia to India, Europe to North America. With its accounts of life changed utterly, lives abruptly finished; testimonies of the poignancy, the loneliness and sometimes madness of lockdown, this book is an essential statement of record on the dark times we are living through.

€12 (free postage worldwide for Southword subscribers)
€15 (including postage to Ireland /Europe / North America)
€17 (including postage to Africa / Asia / Australia / South America)

Available to order from www.munsterlit.ie

# Queer Love: An Anthology of Irish Fiction

Queer Love seeks to go some way to redress the lack of acknowledgement of the LGBTQI+ community in Irish literary anthologies, with a mixture of established writers of international standing, writers who have been making a splash in recent years and new emerging writers. The anthology has a mixture of previously published stories, newly commissioned work and those entered through our call out. Featuring stories by John Boyne, Emma Donoghue, Mary Dorcey, Neil Hegarty, James Hudson, Emer Lyons, Jamie O'Connell, Colm Tóibín, Declan Toohey, and Shannon Yee.

€12 (free postage worldwide for Southword subscribers)
€15 (including postage to Ireland /Europe / North America)
€17 (including postage to Africa / Asia / Australia / South America)

Available to order from www.munsterlit.ie

# The Gregory O'Donoghue
# International Poetry Competition

Judge: Thomas McCarthy

1st Prize:
€2,000
publication in *Southword* 42

2nd Prize:
€500
publication in *Southword* 42

3rd Prize:
€250
publication in *Southword* 42

Ten runners-up will be published in *Southword* 42
and receive a €50 publication fee

The competition is open to original, unpublished poems in the English
language of 40 lines or fewer. The poem can be on any subject, in any style,
by a writer of any nationality, living anywhere in the world.

# Deadline: 30th November, 2021
## Guidelines: www.munsterlit.ie

# Subscribers' Free to Enter Competitions (Flash Fiction & Poetry)

Judge: Patrick Cotter (www.patrickcotter.ie)

## Flash Fiction

A single file from each subscriber with no more than three flash fictions will be accepted (250 word limit)

Three winners will be selected and published in Southword 42

1st Prize €150, 2nd prize €100, 3rd prize €75

## Poetry

A single file from each subscriber with no more than three poems will be accepted (40 line limit)

Three winners will be selected and published in Southword 42

1st Prize €150, 2nd prize €100, 3rd prize €75

Current subscribers (as of November 2021) will be emailed a Submittable portal link which will open from 30th November to 31st December 2021.

# Deadline: 31st December, 2021
See issue 40 for last year's winners

# Contributors

**Graham Allen** is a Professor in the School of English, UCC. He is the author of three poetry collections, *The One That Got Away* (2014), *The Madhouse System* (2016) and *Holes: Decade 1* (2017).

**Animashaun Ameen** is a Nigerian poet and essayist. His writings are mostly centered on memory, sexuality, and identity. He lives and writes from Lagos, Nigeria. An oddball. A butterfly. He tweets @AmeenAnimashaun

**Madeline Beach Carey** is the author of the story collection *Les filles dels altres.* Born in Baltimore, Maryland, she lives in Barcelona, Spain with her husband and their fox terrier.

**Susie Berg** is a former co-curator of the Plasticine Poetry reading series, and the author of two full-length poetry collections and three chapbooks. Find her at susieberg.ca or @SusieDBerg.

**Dermot Bolger** is a Dublin-born poet, novelist and playwright. His fourteenth novel, *An Ark of Light* appeared in 2018. His new poetry collection, *Other People's Lives*, will appear in 2022.

**Paddy Bushe** lives in Kerry. *Peripheral Vision*, a collection in English, and *Second Sight*, a selection of his poems in Irish with his own translations, appeared from Dedalus in 2020.

**Patrick Chapman**'s eight poetry collections include *Slow Clocks of Decay* (2016) and *Open Season on the Moon* (2019). His next collection, *The Following Year*, will appear from Salmon in 2022.

**Emily Cooper** is a poet and essayist living in Donegal. Her first poetry collection *Glass* was published by Makina Book in 2021.

**Rachel Coventry**'s poems have appeared in The *North, The Moth, Poetry Ireland Review* and *The Irish Times*. Her debut collection *Afternoon Drinking in the Jolly Butchers* (2018) is published by Salmon poetry.

**Jake Crist** works full-time for a supportive housing nonprofit in Columbus, Ohio. His poems have appeared widely in U.S. publications.

Originally from Limerick, **Majella Cullinane** lives in Port Chalmers, New Zealand. She's won the Kerrygold Prize for Short Fiction and been highly commended in the Seán O'Faolain Short Story Competition and the Sargeson Short Story Prize, NZ.

**Patrick Deeley** has published seven collections with Dedalus Press, the latest being *The End of the World*. He is the 2019 winner of the Lawrence O'Shaughnessy Award.

**Christopher DeWeese** is the author of three books of poetry, most recently *The Confessions* (Periplum Poetry).

**Michael Dooley**'s poems have appeared in publications such as *Poetry Ireland Review, The Stinging Fly, Banshee*, online at RTE Culture, and elsewhere. He is a teacher, and lives in Limerick. www.michaeldooleypoetry.com

**William Doreski** lives in Peterborough, New Hampshire. His most recent book of poetry is *The Absence of Marie* (2021). His essays, poetry, fiction, and reviews have appeared in many journals.

**Ger Duffy**'s poems have been published by Slow Dancer Press, The Waxed Lemon, Drawn to the Light Press and Vox Galvia. She received a Mentoring Award in Poetry in 2021.

**Orla Fay** is the editor of Drawn to the Light Press. She is the Poetry Town Laureate for Dunshaughlin, County Meath. Her debut collection is forthcoming from Salmon Poetry. Twitter @FayOrla

**Bernadette Gallagher** was born in County Donegal, travelled east and west before taking root in County Cork. Her poetry is available in printed and online journals. bernadettegallagher.blogspot.ie

**Daniel Hinds**' poetry has been published or is forthcoming in *The London Magazine, The New European, Wild Court, Poetry Salzburg Review, Stand, The Honest Ulsterman, Abridged*, and elsewhere. Twitter: @DanielGHinds

**Patrick Holloway** is the recent winner of the Molly Keane Creative Writing Award. He won second place in The Raymond Carver Short Story Contest and was the winner of HeadStuff Poem of the Year.

**Lucy Holme** lives in Cork. Her debut chapbook, due in August 2022 from Broken Sleep Books, was shortlisted for The Patrick Kavanagh Award. She is studying for an MA in Creative Writing at University College Cork.

**Manuel Igrejas.** Fiction: In the anthologies *Men on Men 4* and *Image OutWrte*. Poetry: *A New Geography of Poets*. Plays: *Shrinkage, Kitty and Lina, Miss Mary Dugan, Hassan and Sylvia, Margarita and Max, Instimacy, Doofus, Chair, How To Make A Million, Who Am I?* and *Pittsburgh!*

**Alice Jolly** has won the Pen Ackerley Prize and the V.S. Pritchett Memorial Prize. She was runner up for the Rathbones Folio Prize in 2019 and won an O. Henry Award in 2021.

**V.P. Loggins** is the author of *The Wild Severance* (Bright Hill Press, 2021), *The Green Cup* (Cider Press Review, 2017), *The Fourth Paradise* (Main Street Rag, 2010), and *Heaven Changes* (2007, Pudding House).

**Peadar Lamb** is an artist working primarily in the medium of stained glass for over twenty years. Using hand-made glass, he employs a variety of techniques (some of which have changed little since the 11th century), such as acid etching, painting and staining, in novel ways to create contemporary unique pieces.

**Sandy Longley**'s poems have appeared in *Nimrod International Journal, Southword, Strokestown Poetry Anthology, Spillway* and others. She was a Robert Frost Foundation Prize finalist. *Navigating the Waters* was published by Finishing Line Press.

**Bernadette McCarthy**'s poetry has appeared in journals including *Agenda, Crannog, The London Magazine, The Penny Dreadful,* and *Poetry Ireland Review,* as well as various anthologies. Her chapbook *Bog Arabic* was published by Southword Editions in 2018.

**Peggy McCarthy** won the Fish Poetry Prize 2020. She has had work published in The Chair of Ireland Poetry Commemorative Anthology 2020. She lives in Waterford city.

**Sarah McCartt-Jackson** is a Kentucky poet, folklorist, and educator. Her poetry books include: *Stonelight, Calf Canyon, Vein of Stone,* and *Children Born on the Wrong Side of the River.*

**Kate McHugh** is 21-year-old student from Galway, currently pursuing an undergraduate degree in Creative Writing, English and French at NUIG, and has been previously published in *ROPES*.

**Dante Micheaux** is the author of *Circus* (2018), which won the Four Quartets Prize from the Poetry Society of America and the T. S. Eliot Foundation and *Amorous Shepherd* (2010).

**Immanuel Mifsud** is a national literary award winner, recipient of the European Union Prize for Literature, and a founding member of PEN Malta. He lectures at the University of Malta.

**Gerry Murphy**'s latest collection is *The Humours of Nothingness* (Dedalus Press, 2020).

An avid solo-traveller and outdoor enthusiast, **Fenella O'Regan** (23) is currently based in the Canary Islands where she is honing both her literary and Spanish skills beneath blue skies.

**Mary O'Donnell** is a poet, short-story writer, and novelist who lives in Kildare. Novels include *Where They Lie*. Short story collections include *Storm Over Belfast* and *Empire*. She holds a PhD in Creative Writing from University College Cork.

Published and anthologized in numerous, international outlets, **Kimberly Reyes** writes about identity, ecology, and sexuality, and spends her time between Ireland, San Francisco and New York City.

**Mark Roper**'s collection, *Bindweed* (2017), was shortlisted for the Irish Times Poetry Now Award. *A Gather of Shadow* (2012), also shortlisted for that award, won the Michael Hartnett Award, 2014.

**Kathrin Schmidt** is a multi-award-winning poet and writer. Her novel *You're not dying* (2009) won the German Book Prize and was translated into 13 languages. GDR-born, her voice is feminist and political.

**Lydia Searle** grew up in Yorkshire and lives in Belfast. She has a BA in Literature and Creative Writing from Goldsmiths College and works for a charity with care-experienced young people.

**Fiona B. Smith** has had poetry published in *Southword, Poetry Ireland Review, Crannog, The Stony Thursday Book, Hennessy New Irish Writing*, the Templar Poetry Anthology *Skein* and the *Over the Edge* anthology.

**Heather Treseler** is the author of *Parturition*, which received the Munster Literature Centre's Fool for Poetry chapbook prize. In 2021, Spencer Reece chose her poem *Wildlife* for the W. B. Yeats Prize.

**Niamh Twomey** is a poet from Clare. Her work has most recently appeared in *New Irish Writing*. She holds an MA in Creative Writing from University College Cork.

**Sue Vickerman**'s translation of Schmidt's story collection *It's over. Don't go there* will be published in 2021. She also translated the chapbook *Twenty Poems* by Kathrin Schmidt (Arc Publications, 2020).

**Mark Ward** is the author of the chapbooks *Circumference* (Finishing Line), *Carcass* (Seven Kitchens) and *Hike* (Bear Creek). His full-length collection, *Nightlight*, is out from Salmon Poetry in summer 2022. www.astintinyourspotlight.wordpress.com

**Ruth Ward** is a member of PEN America. Her works have been published, performed, or translated in sixteen countries. Her creative collaborations center on the Mediterranean, particularly Spain and Malta.

# How to Submit

*Southword* welcomes unsolicited submissions of original work in fiction and poetry during the following open submission periods:

POETRY

| | |
|---|---|
| What to submit: | Up to four poems in a single file |
| When to submit: | 1st December, 2021 – 28th February, 2022 |
| Payment: | *Southword* will pay €40 per poem |

FICTION

| | |
|---|---|
| What to submit: | One short story (no longer than 5,000 words) |
| When to submit: | 1st January – 31st March, 2022 |
| Payment: | *Southword* will pay €250 for a short story of up to 5,000 words |

Submissions will be accepted through our Submittable portal online.
Visit www.southword.submittable.com for further guidelines.

Printed in Great Britain
by Amazon

79119108R00073